Lust, hot 

pore of Z

It heated her f... an exquisitely ... awareness of Aiden's body. She wallowed in the strength of the arms carrying her; the warm wet wall of chest pressing against the sides of her breast.

He was taking her to his place, she knew. Into a hot shower, he'd said, the setting of one of her wildest fantasies about him. *Oh God.*

She felt weak with desire, driven by cravings so strong they amazed her. She wasn't used to wanting a man this much. Lust, she decided, was nothing at all like love.

Lust focused on one thing and on one thing only.

The physical.

'Glad to see you're still alive,' he teased when she opened her eyes. 'I was just about to do mouth-to-mouth resuscitation.'

The thought of his mouth on hers banished what little scruples she had left. She couldn't hide her feelings any longer.

'I'd have liked that,' she whispered, a ripple of excitement ricocheting down her spine.

He was taken aback. But only for a second or two.

Lowering the strap of her swimsuit, he took her mouth in deep possession…

Dear Reader,

Welcome to super-sexy Blaze™!

If your preference is for fast and furious, hot and outrageous love stories then this is the line for you.

We leap in at the deep end this month with a sizzling story centring on two fiery protagonists who have few inhibitions—when with each other! This latest amazing HOT CITY NIGHTS tale—*Uninhibited*—is based in the elegant city of Boston, compliments of Candace Schuler. Don't forget there's one HOT CITY NIGHTS story every month.

Our second Blaze is from the talented pen of fabulous author Miranda Lee. *Just A Little Sex...* starts with one night of passion that would fulfil all of your wildest fantasies but turns into so much more!

You're not going to be able to put them down!

Love,

The Editors

JUST A LITTLE SEX...

by

Miranda Lee

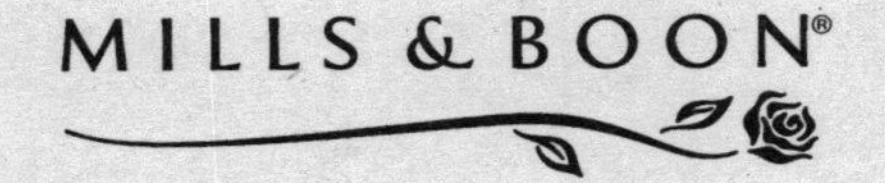

All the characters in this book have no existence outside the imagination of the author, and have no relation whatsoever to anyone bearing the same name or names. They are not even distantly inspired by any individual known or unknown to the author, and all the incidents are pure invention.

First published in Great Britain 2001
by Harlequin Mills & Boon Limited,
Eton House, 18-24 Paradise Road, Richmond, Surrey TW9 1SR

ISBN 0 263 82884 0

14-1201

Printed and bound in Spain
by Litografia Rosés S.A., Barcelona

For Tony

My inspiration

Dear Reader,

Since you've picked up this book and you're reading this, then we already have one thing in common. We like our romance hot! Trust me when I say *Just a Little Sex...* is hot. When I first heard about the Blaze™ books, with their extra-sexy tone and extra-sexy storylines, I suspected Mills & Boon® might have invented this line just for me. Not only were these love stories required to have super-sexy storylines, but they were longer than usual. Wow! All those extra pages to explore my erotic fantasies to the full. I couldn't wait to try my hand at one.

I was over the moon when Zoe and Aiden's romance was not only accepted, but also chosen as one of the early books to help launch this new series. I am very proud of my first Blaze and hope you find reading *Just a Little Sex...* as exciting and satisfying an experience as I did writing it.

Miranda Lee

1

ZOE didn't have one hint of premonition as she stepped out of her office building and headed for her lunchtime meeting with Drake. Everything seemed wonderful in her world.

At long last.

Five years it had been since she'd come to Sydney from the country, a plump naive twenty-year-old with so many hopes and dreams. What a learning curve that first year had been! Hard to think about some of the things which had happened to her without wincing. Greg was the worst memory. What a louse he'd turned out to be!

Still, she'd survived, hadn't she? And she'd come through it with even more determination than ever to make a success of her life, to become the woman she'd always wanted to be.

Okay, so it had taken her another four years of driving and depriving herself, of crummy day jobs and endless night schools; of diets and grueling workouts at the gym.

But it had been worth it, hadn't it? she told herself as she strode down George Street in the direction of the harbor. She looked pretty darned good, even if she said so herself. She had a challenging job, a fab place to live, and best of all, she'd finally landed herself one fantastic boyfriend.

Drake was everything she'd ever dreamed about. Not only was he tall, dark and handsome, he was a success at his job and had money to burn. His most wonderful feature, however, was that he was mad about her.

Sometimes, she could hardly believe her luck.

They'd met four months ago when he'd been selling her boss a plush inner-city apartment. That was Drake's job, selling apartments in the high-rise buildings which had been mushrooming up all over Sydney's central business district, capitalizing on the growing number of professionals who wanted to live near the city and didn't care what they paid for the privilege. Drake had literally made a fortune in commissions and had been able to afford to buy one of those same luxury apartments for himself.

He'd asked Zoe out the very first day they'd met, claiming later it was love at first sight. Zoe had been a little wary at first—once bitten, definitely twice shy—but it wasn't long before Drake was the main focus of her life. Gone were the long lonely weekends. Gone, the depressing moments when she wondered what on earth she was doing with her life. Gone, the fear that she would never experience the sort of love and romance every girl dreamed of experiencing.

Gone. Gone. Gone!

Zoe glanced at her watch when the lights at the next intersection turned red. Twenty-three minutes past twelve.

She frowned.

It was normally only a ten-minute walk from her building down to the Rocks area and the restaurant where she regularly met Drake for lunch. The Rockery was his favorite harborside eating place, a trendy little bistro on the upper floor of a converted warehouse. He'd said to meet him there right on twelve-thirty today and not to be late, because he only had an hour.

Drake hated being kept waiting, even for a few minutes. Zoe supposed this impatience came from being a perfectionist. And a planner. She was a bit like that herself.

It seemed ages before the lights turned green again. Zoe hurried across the street, her heart racing for fear of being late. But she made it down to the restaurant with three minutes to spare.

Fortunately, Drake had not yet arrived so she made a dash to the ladies' room for repairs, where her reflection in the mirror showed a perspiration-beaded forehead and wind-ruffled hair.

That was the trouble with walking. Still, it only took a few strokes of her brush and a fluff-up with her fingers to make her hair fall back into its chic auburn-tinted, shoulder-length, multi-layered, face-framing style. She'd had it cut and colored by one of Sydney's top hairdressers, who charged a small fortune. But the end result was well worth the money.

Admittedly, she had to rise almost an hour earlier every morning to get ready for work these days. Blow-drying her willfully wavy hair straight was not a quick process. Neither was applying the sort of makeup which covered every flaw, looked almost natural and didn't require constant touch-ups during the day.

Except when you sprinted down George Street on a warm summer's day.

A swift dabbing of translucent powder over her slightly melted foundation, a refreshing of her lipstick, and she was ready.

Another glance at her watch showed she was now officially one minute late. When she emerged Zoe groaned to find Drake already sitting at their regular table by the window, tapping his fingers on the crisp white tablecloth.

Darn, darn and double darn!

Dredging up a bright smile, Zoe hurried toward him. His head swiveled her way, his dark eyes definitely displeased. Zoe couldn't help some exasperation of her own. Truly, anyone would think he'd been waiting half an hour instead of a couple of minutes at best.

She mouthed an apology as she approached and his scowl metamorphed into a marvelous smile, his eyes full of admiration as they raked over her slender gym-honed body, encased that day in a chic black-and-white silk shift dress.

Zoe's inner tension vanished in an instant. She loved it when he looked at her like that; like she was the most beautiful girl in the world.

Yet she knew she wasn't. She'd simply worked very hard on her body and learned how to make the best of herself.

Drake, she realized with a sudden flash of insight,

was of a similar ilk. Although attractive, he had several physical flaws which he'd learned to hide, or which you didn't notice once he turned his charm on full wattage, as he was doing now. His dazzling smile and dancing black eyes distracted from the fact his nose was too large and his lips a bit on the thin side. The superbly tailored suits he always wore masked his less-than-perfect frame, providing broader shoulders than he actually possessed. Although he did weights in the gym and was very fit and toned, Drake did not have a great natural shape.

Not that Zoe cared. She would have been the last person on earth to judge anyone by their body alone.

''Now that's a sight worth waiting for,'' he complimented warmly, rising to go 'round and pull out her chair for her.

''I really was here on time,'' she said as she sat down. ''But the wind had done dreadful things to my hair.''

''Looks perfect to me. There again,'' he added on his return to his own chair, his gaze still appreciative, ''you always look perfect to me.''

Zoe laughed. ''You should see me first thing in the morning.''

One of his dark brows arched. ''But I have, haven't I? And I can testify you look even more beautiful then.''

Zoe smiled a little sheepishly at this particular compliment. That was because she always crept into the bathroom before he woke up and fixed her face and hair before slipping back into his bed.

Her fear of Drake seeing her at less than her physical best was deep, and probably irrational, given that he truly loved her. But she couldn't help it. Goodness knew what she would do if he ever asked her to have a shower with him!

"They say love is blind," she quipped.

"I don't think so. Not with me, anyway. When I look at you, I know exactly what I see. The perfect woman. You're beautiful. Smart. Sexy. But best of all, you know what you want in life and are prepared to work hard to get it. You've no idea how attractive I find that." He reached over the table and picked up her left hand, stroking its perfectly manicured fingers. "I'm crazy about you, Zoe."

Her heart melted as it always did when he told her things like that. "And I'm crazy about you," she returned softly.

"Then why won't you move in with me?"

Zoe smothered a sigh. This was the second time Drake had brought this subject up.

The offer was flattering, she supposed, but not what she wanted at this time in her life. Zoe had just discovered dating and romance, and she didn't want to give it up just yet. She knew what happened when people started living together. Soon, they were taking each other for granted or arguing about the housework.

Alternatively, the girl did everything then resented her boyfriend like mad. Zoe had been an unpaid, unappreciated housekeeper for her father for several years, and once was enough!

But she could hardly tell Drake that. It would sound...selfish.

''Drake, look, I'm sorry,'' she said gently. ''I love you to death. And I love the time we spend together. But I'd rather leave things as they are for now. I mean...we haven't known each other all that long, have we? And living with each other is a very big step.''

His lips pressed tightly together and Zoe felt a moment of panic. Was this it? Was he going to dump her, just because she wouldn't live with him?

Drake eventually cocked his head on one side and smiled a wry smile. ''Is this your way of playing hard to get again?''

Zoe blinked. ''What do you mean?''

''Well, it took me two months to get you into bed. That's a record, believe me. I was beginning to think you were frigid.''

Zoe suspected her refusal to sleep with Drake had only made him keener, but she honestly hadn't been playing a game. The truth was her relationship with the ghastly Greg had left her with a host of insecurities and an appalling self-body image. Despite now having a figure most women would envy, she'd still needed to be endlessly pursued and flattered by Drake before feeling confident enough to expose herself physically to him.

He'd finally succeeded in seducing her, courtesy of two bottles of wine over dinner, two hours of foreplay and umpteen declarations of devoted and undying love for her.

Being frigid hadn't been the issue at all.

Of course, Zoe had to concede she wasn't crash-hot in bed. How could she be when her only other experience had been with a wham-bang-thank-you-ma'am kind of man? Drake's well-practiced technique in bed had been a real eye-opener. When she'd even had an orgasm that first night, she'd been over the moon.

Unfortunately, once she returned to being stone-cold sober, having a climax during sex became as scarce as chocolate éclairs in her diet.

Not Drake's fault of course. He was a wonderful lover. Attentive and tender and romantic, always doing and saying the right things. The blame lay entirely with her. Once naked, she always worried too much about what she looked like. Exercise and dieting might have gotten rid of the fat and the flab, but not those wretched old tapes playing in her head.

Thinking negative thoughts about herself was obviously a killer when it came to coming.

When her not having orgasms began to bother Drake, Zoe did the only thing a sensible girl in love could do. She started faking them. After all, why should Drake have to feel guilty or inadequate when the inadequacies were all hers?

And who knew? Maybe one day, when she felt *really* relaxed and not the result of an alcoholic coma; when all her old doubts and fears had been firmly routed, she would come like clockwork. 'Til then, Zoe wasn't going to stress over one small imperfection in their relationship which had nothing whatsoever to do with Drake and everything to do with her own personal physical hang-ups.

"Have you ordered?" she asked, deftly changing the subject away from moving in with him.

''First thing I did.''

The drinks waiter appeared on cue, with a glass of chilled Chardonnay for Zoe and Drake's usual lunch-time liquid of mineral water. He never drank when he had to return to work.

''I've ordered the food, too,'' he added when Zoe went to pick up the menu.

''Oh.'' Zoe tried not to feel irritated, because once again, she only had herself to blame. During her first half dozen dinner dates with Drake, she'd always deferred to his greater knowledge of wine and food, and now, he often presumed to order for her.

''I couldn't wait for you to arrive,'' he said, perhaps seeing her slight annoyance. ''I told you. I don't have much time. I have to pick up a client at the Hyatt at one-thirty. Businessman from Hong Kong. Wants a penthouse smack-dab in the middle of Sydney. Money no object.''

''Wow. Sounds like a good prospect.''

''You can say that again. Sydney's moved up a notch in popularity since the Olympics. And why not? It's the best city in the world. And the most beautiful.''

''You don't have to sell me on Sydney,'' Zoe commented. ''I love the place. Just look at that view.'' From where she was sitting, Zoe could see the Opera House on her right and the bridge on her left. Straight ahead, a sleek white cruiser was slicing through the sparkling blue waters, its decks filled with photo-snapping tourists.

Zoe was sipping her wine and admiring the view

herself when she heard Drake suck in sharply, as though in shock.

Her eyes snapped back to find him staring at something—or someone. She heard him mutter under his breath.

Zoe swiveled 'round in her chair to see firsthand the object of Drake's agitation.

She was blond, and she was heading their way.

Zoe didn't recognize the woman and she would have, if they'd met before. Stunning six-foot blondes with double-D-cup breasts were hard to forget.

"Well, well, well," the blond bombshell said with a saccharine smile as she stopped beside their table. It took a moment for her impressive cleavage to jiggle to a halt. "If it isn't Drake Carson, the man of a thousand lines and even more broken promises. Sorry to interrupt, honey," she directed at Zoe, "but Drake and I have some unfinished business. You did say you'd call, didn't you, lover? I mean, I know it's only been a couple of weeks since the conference, but I was beginning to think you hadn't found me quite so *special* after all. Surely you aren't one of those creeps who lie their teeth out to get a girl into bed, the type who thinks they can do what they like when they go away, without any consequences and without the little woman back home finding out?"

Drake glowered at her but said nothing.

Zoe felt like a big black pit had yawned underneath her chair and she was about to fall in. Drake had gone to a sales and marketing conference in Melbourne just two weeks earlier. He'd rung her every night of the three days he'd been away, saying how much he'd missed her.

She stared at him, wanting to believe this woman was some crazed jealous troublemaker intent on breaking them up for her own devious reasons. But the cornered guilt on Drake's face simply could not be ignored. Or denied.

''Oh, so you *are* one of those creeps?'' the blonde taunted. ''Well, I never! Aren't you lucky I'm not a vengeful bitch like that blond chick in that movie? What was it? *Fatal Attraction?* I mean, the way I see it, if a guy's a liar and a cheat, I don't really want any more to do with him.'' She turned back to face Zoe. ''Gee, honey, you're looking a little pale. Don't tell me you're the little woman back home. What a shame. And you look real nice, too. Poor you. 'Bye, 'bye, Drake. Have a nice day.''

Zoe watched, dry-mouthed, as the blonde stalked back to where a tall, elderly man was waiting for her near reception. He was frowning like he didn't now what was going on. The blonde whispered something to him, took his arm and they both left.

Drake still hadn't said a single word, but his eyes told it all.

Zoe felt sick. And stunned. And shattered.

''You slept with her, didn't you?'' she choked out. ''At the Melbourne conference.''

''It wasn't like she said,'' he muttered, not meeting her eyes.

''Then how was it?'' Zoe heard herself ask in a cold flat voice. She couldn't believe this was happening to her again. She could have sworn that Drake was nothing like Greg; that he truly loved her; that their relationship was not just a cruel joke.

His eyes lifted from the tablecloth. Panicky, pleading eyes. ''God, Zoe, don't look at me like that. I love you, darling. Honest.''

She winced at the darling. ''Then you have a funny way of showing it,'' she bit out, ''making love to another woman.''

''But I didn't make love to her. You're the only woman I make love to. It was just sex. It meant nothing. *She* meant nothing.''

Zoe despised men who said things like that. ''She obviously thought she did,'' she pointed out tartly, ''or she wouldn't have been so hurt.''

''Don't bet on it,'' he countered, his cheeks flushed with anger. ''Some women are right bitches. Believe me, she knew the score. She knew it was just a one-night stand right from the start, and now, for her own warped reasons, she's pretending it was something else.''

Zoe shook her head which was a bad move. It was already spinning. ''How can you possibly be in love with me and go to bed with another woman? *How?*''

Drake began to look belligerent, as he did when someone expressed an opinion different to his own. ''I told you. It was just sex. There's a big difference. Love and sex don't always have to go together, Zoe. I thought you'd know that by now. You're not a baby. You're twenty-five years old. Hey, Zoe, *try* to understand.'' His hands lifted to rake through his thick black hair. They were actually trembling.

For the first time since that blonde dropped her

bombshell, Zoe began to believe that Drake might love her, despite everything.

''I'm sorry,'' he went on urgently. ''More sorry than you can ever imagine. But it wasn't like she said. I'm not some kind of serial sleazebag. I was just weak for a moment. You're the one I love, Zoe. Too much perhaps. I was missing you terribly and wanting you like mad. I couldn't stop thinking about you and it got me so darned horny. It happened on the last night of the conference. We'd all been drinking heavily.''

''You never drink at *all* when socializing at work,'' she reminded him with a rush of anger, not wanting to be soothed by excuses and explanations. Didn't he understand what he'd done? He could call it whatever he liked but he'd still been intimate with another woman. And whispered sweet nothings in her ear while he'd been doing it.

Perhaps that hurt even more than his actual physical betrayal. The things he must have said.

''The conference was virtually over,'' he continued explaining. ''I didn't have to drive anywhere so I let my hair down for once. Look, she threw herself at me. Followed me into the elevator at the end of the night. Practically ravished me then and there. I hated myself afterward, but what can I say? I'm not a saint. I'm just a man. I made a mistake. I'm so terribly sorry, Zoe. I never meant to hurt you. I never thought you'd find out.''

''Obviously.'' She could no longer look at him. All she could think about now was that blonde and him, doing it in an elevator of all places. How tacky!

''Don't be like that, Zoe. *Try* to understand.''

''I don't think I can,'' she said wretchedly. Which meant there was nothing left to do but to split up with Drake. She'd vowed after Greg that she'd never put up with a man treating her badly ever again. Which was why she'd been manless and dateless for almost four long years.

Still, the thought of going back to a single lifestyle made her shudder. She didn't want to be that lonely ever again. She'd thought she never would be. She thought she had Drake. She thought after a couple of years of their being girlfriend and boyfriend, they'd eventually get married and have kids and live happily ever after.

A sob broke from her throat, tears stinging her eyes.

Drake groaned. ''Don't cry, darling. Please don't cry. If you forgive me,'' he urged, reaching over the table and grabbing her hands, ''it won't ever happen again. I promise.''

A sudden and overwhelming wave of bitterness had Zoe yanking her hands away from his. ''And what happens the next time you're at a conference, and some sexy-looking blonde with big boobs throws herself at you?''

''I'll know what I'm risking if I go with her, so I won't.''

Zoe stared at him with pained confusion in her eyes. ''But you'd still *want* to?''

He groaned again. ''For pity's sake, Zoe. I'm only thirty years old. I'm a normal red-blooded male in his sexual prime. Loving you doesn't mean I won't ever be physically attracted to another woman ever again.

That's unrealistic and unnatural. But I give you my word, I will never act on any such attraction ever again.''

Zoe stared at him. She wanted to believe him. She really did.

But then she thought of that blonde and what she had said in parting.

Poor you.

''I think,'' she said tautly, ''that I'll skip lunch and go for a walk. I need some fresh air. And time to think.''

''Please don't do that, Zoe. Stay and talk to me.''

Zoe shook her head then bent to pick up her handbag. Staying and talking to Drake was the last thing she should do. He was too good a talker. Too good a salesman. Perhaps too good a liar.

''We can work this out, Zoe,'' he insisted. ''Truly we can. I don't want to lose you, darling. I love you. And I know you love me.''

She glared at him. ''Yes, but your idea of love and my idea of love are poles apart. I know I would never have done what you did. Never, no matter what the circumstances.''

''Isn't there anything I can say to make you understand?''

''Not right now.''

''What about later?''

''Leave it for today, Drake.''

''I can't. I'll call 'round tonight after you get home from work.''

''If you must.''

''I must. I won't let you go, Zoe. I mean it.''

''I know you do,'' she said. Which was another reason why she needed to get away from him. Because she feared Drake would talk her into forgiving him without her ever understanding what had happened, and why? Love was a very weakening emotion. In a woman, anyway.

She stood up just as the waiter arrived with their meals. For a split second, Zoe was tempted to stay and shovel every morsel of the delicious-looking food down her throat.

Misery always made her hungry.

But being overweight had made her even more miserable, so she knew there would be no comfort for her there. No comfort in Drake's presence, either. She wanted to strangle him for doing this to her, for spoiling everything, for being a typical male.

She'd thought he was different. Deeper.

But he wasn't.

''I have to go,'' she said raggedly, and fled.

2

ZOE didn't go for a walk. When she felt more tears threatening, she headed straight back for the office, making it to the downstairs lobby of the multi-storyed building in six minutes flat. She kept a tight grip on herself in the ride up in the elevator, since she wasn't alone, but could feel her control slipping by the time the doors whooshed back on the twelfth floor.

Unfortunately, the rooms which housed Phillips & Cox, Attorneys at Law, were right down the end of a corridor along which more people were coming and going. It was lunchtime, after all.

Crying was not an option 'til she had total privacy.

Clenching her jaw to keep her chin from quivering, Zoe launched herself down the gray-carpeted hallway, delivering a plastic smile whenever she passed an acquaintance.

Finally, she made it, only to find that June, their receptionist, was eating lunch at her desk, instead of in the café downstairs, as she usually did.

"What are you doing back so early?" June probed when Zoe walked back in. "Weren't you supposed to be having lunch with the boyfriend down at the Rockery?"

Zoe's teeth clenched even harder in her jaw.

''He was called back to work early,'' she managed with feigned nonchalance, ''so I thought I'd come back and have my coffee here.''

''Silly you. I'd have stayed down there. The coffee here is just instant muck. You could have had the real McCoy at the Rockery.''

''Oh, well...'' Zoe shrugged, smiled an indifferent smile, then sped down to the tearoom, hoping it would be blessedly deserted and she could have a good quiet cry. But as luck would have it, her boss was there, making coffee and muttering away to herself. 'Til she saw Zoe.

''What on earth are you doing back so early?'' Fran asked. ''I thought you were having lunch with Drake?''

It was too much for Zoe.

Fran literally gaped when Zoe burst into tears. In the six months Zoe had worked for her, the girl had never cried once. Or even seemed flustered. She was so cool and competent that sometimes Fran forgot she was only twenty-five.

Fran was not by nature a soft or sympathetic person, but she'd had considerable experience in handling weeping females. Considerable experience in the cause of such weeping as well. Her part of the practice specialized in divorce cases.

Fran didn't have to be told that a man was behind Zoe's tears. And there was only one man in Zoe's life. The very charming and successful Drake Carson.

Plucking a handful of tissues from the box sitting on the counter, Fran pressed them into her assistant's hands, then led the weeping girl back to her office.

Fortunately, this didn't require going past June, who was the office gossip.

"Sit," she ordered, pushing Zoe down into one of the large comfy chairs facing her desk before returning to her own black office chair. There, she waited patiently 'til the worst of the weeping was over.

Zoe's sobbing eventually subsided to a sniffle.

"Can I get you something?" Fran asked at that point, her tone matter-of-fact. "Coffee? Brandy? A hit man?"

Zoe's head jerked up and she laughed a rueful laugh.

"Want to tell me about it?" Fran said.

Zoe looked at her boss and suddenly saw, not just the smart-as-a-whip lawyer, but the woman. Thirty-eight and still very attractive, with jet-black hair—cut into a short chic bob—piercing gray eyes, a pale unlined skin and an hourglass figure which looked good in the severe black suits she favoured. Highly respected by her colleagues and clients, she was married to Angus Phillips, the senior partner in the firm.

But what about before that? She must have had other men, a woman like her. Plenty of them. She'd seen so much more of life than Zoe. She might be able to explain what had happened between Drake and that blonde so that Zoe could forgive him and go on as before.

Because that was what she really wanted to do. Now that she'd had time to think about it, breaking up with Drake was just too horrendous to contemplate.

So she told her boss what had happened. Fran listened without interruption, her face not giving away a thing. But Zoe suspected she wasn't shocked. Which shocked Zoe.

"Aren't you surprised?" she said at last.

Fran smiled a dry smile. "Nothing men do ever surprises me, Zoe. The more attractive the man, the less I'm surprised. So no, I'm not surprised. I think it's a shame, however, that you found out about Drake's little indiscretion. If you hadn't, you'd still be perfectly happy with him."

"But...but...it wasn't just a little indiscretion. He was unfaithful. And more than once, I suspect. I don't believe for a moment he only slept with that woman on just the last night."

"Why? Was she so very beautiful?"

"She was stunning, with the biggest boobs I've ever seen outside of one of those magazines."

"Maybe he has a secret boob fetish. Or maybe she gave him something you don't. Forgive me for prying, Zoe, but I can't advise you without knowing all the facts. Are you sure you satisfy Drake in bed?"

Zoe floundered at this point. "I...I thought I did."

"Why? Because you have sex a lot?"

"Well...isn't that the main criterion?" Zoe had always been under the impression that most men complained that they weren't getting enough.

"Not necessarily. Some men are more interested in quality rather than quantity. They like different positions. Different places. You're not one of those silly girls who insist on always doing it in bed with the lights out, do you?"

''Of course not,'' she denied hotly. And in truth, she didn't.

It was Drake's idea that they always do it in bed. He was big on creating a romantic atmosphere with satin sheets and scented candles and soft dreamy music.

Not that she wasn't happy with the arrangement. Zoe liked comfort. And candlelight was so very flattering. As for different positions… Zoe was more than grateful that Drake didn't want to do it doggie-style on the floor, or up against the wall in the shower or with her on top.

Even *thinking* of the physical exposure such positions would inflict on her made her cringe.

Now she wondered if Drake had secretly craved doing it in just those ways all along, but hadn't wanted to ask. It had taken a brazen blonde in an elevator to fulfil his sexual fantasies.

''What about oral sex?'' Fran persisted, and Zoe could feel herself blushing. But it did seem odd having this very frank conversation with her boss when up 'til today, their relationship had been strictly professional.

''It's…er…not my favorite form of foreplay,'' she confessed. She'd done it once. Sort of. For about twenty seconds. But thankfully, Drake stopped her before the unthinkable happened. He'd never asked for it again, or steered her that way a second time, and she certainly wasn't going to do it off her own bat.

''I don't think it's Drake's, either,'' she added, a touch defensively.

"Really? That's unusual. Most men are pretty keen. But I guess it takes all types and you'd know your boyfriend best."

"I thought I did," Zoe said wretchedly. "Maybe I don't know him at all. Maybe our whole relationship is a sham. Maybe he's having affairs right, left and center."

"I don't think so, Zoe. If he was, I'd know about it."

"Huh?"

Fran gave her a droll look. "Angus and I have been living in the same building as Drake since the time you started dating him. We share the same garage, the same elevators, the same swimming pool and gym. I've never seen him with another girl except you. Not once. Clearly, he's not in the habit of two-timing you, or I'd have caught him at it by now."

Zoe brightened a bit at this news. "But what does Drake mean when he says it was *just sex* with that blonde, and that she meant nothing to him? I got the impression he didn't even *like* her. I can't seem to get my mind 'round that concept. How can you have sex with someone you don't even like, or really know? Is it just a male thing? Is that why I can't understand it?"

Fran gave her an incredulous look. "Haven't you ever fantasized about having sex with a stranger, or met a man and been struck with instant lust for him? All you want is to get laid, right then and there. No getting-to-know-you stuff. No prelims. No niceties. Just down-and-dirty sex."

"Good Lord, no," Zoe denied, her face hotting up

again. ‘‘I can’t think of anything worse. I have to at least *like* a man before I can go to bed with him.’’ She’d even liked the ghastly Greg, ’til he’d shown his true colors. ‘‘I haven’t even looked at another man since going out with Drake, let alone want to get laid by one.’’

‘‘You’ve never had a one-night stand?’’

‘‘No. Never.’’

‘‘My, my, you are an original, Zoe. Maybe that’s why Drake is so crazy about you, and doesn’t want to lose you. Such romantic idealism and tunnel-vision loyalty is rare in this day and age. He could trust you anywhere, anytime. Which brings us back to the point. Can *you* ever trust *him* again? Should you or should you not break up with him? Should you believe him when he says he’s sorry, and give him another chance?’’

‘‘That’s exactly my problem,’’ Zoe said unhappily. ‘‘I honestly don’t know what to do.’’

‘‘And I honestly can’t tell you what to do. It has to be your decision. All I can say is I’d like a dollar for every woman I’ve represented who’s later regretted breaking up her marriage over a spot of adultery. She ends up miserable and lonely whilst the husband simply moves on to the other woman.’’

‘‘That’s what I’m afraid of,’’ Zoe mumbled. ‘‘Being miserable and lonely.’’

‘‘Then give him another chance. What have you got to lose?’’

‘‘My pride and self-respect?’’

Fran laughed. ‘‘Most of the divorced women I

know don't find pride and self-respect much solace in their beds at night.''

But it wasn't the sex Zoe was going to miss so much. It was the company. And the sense of purpose. The promise of a happy future together.

She sighed. ''I suppose I will take him back. In the end. But I hate the thought of his being forgiven so easily and so quickly. Drake's coming over after work tonight and I just know he'll talk me 'round in no time flat.''

''You'd rather him suffer a while longer, is that it?''

''Yes, I guess so. Then he might understand how much he hurt me by what he did.''

''You know, that's not such a bad idea,'' Fran said, twisting back and forth on her swivel chair, a thoughtful expression on her face. ''Why don't you go away somewhere for the weekend and not tell him? Let him sweat for a while. Let him worry and wonder over where you are, and who you might be with. I guarantee, when you finally get back, he won't take you for granted ever again.''

The idea did appeal.

''Why not go home for the weekend?'' Fran suggested.

''That'd be the first place Drake would think of. He'd ring there for sure.''

''Haven't you heard of little white lies, Zoe? Just don't answer the phone yourself and get whoever does to say they hadn't seen hide nor hair of you.''

''Yes, I could do that, but the trouble is Betty would ask all sorts of awkward questions.''

"Who's Betty? I thought you were an only child and your dad, a widower."

"I am and he is. Betty's his housekeeper. She's a lovely lady, but she's far too intuitive and too darned good at worming things out of me. I honestly don't want to tell her about this. Drake came home with me at Christmas and he wasn't on his best behavior. He never is when he's bored stiff. I don't want to blot his copybook any further, not if I aim to forgive him."

"Okay, so home's out..." Fran started chewing the end of a biro as she did when working out some legal strategy. Finally, she snapped forward on her chair and stood up. "I have it! I'll ask Nigel if you can use his weekender. He's not going up there this weekend, because he's off to the opening of some play tomorrow night, starring his latest love. Wait here."

Fran was gone before Zoe could say yeah or nay.

Nigel was Nigel Cox, the third partner in the firm. Fortyish and openly gay, he represented several highly paid clients in the entertainment and sporting world. Zoe didn't really have much to do with him. He had his own assistant, as did Angus. She'd heard of the weekender, though. From June, who called it Nigel's little love nest.

Apparently, it overlooked a small beach up near Port Stephens, just far enough off the main tourist route for privacy, but close enough to civilization for essential supplies and services, which meant a good selection of five-star restaurants. Nigel's second favorite hobby in life—according to the ever-knowledgeable June—was gourmet food.

Fran swept back in eventually, carrying a set of keys and two hand-drawn maps.

''Mission accomplished,'' she said, dumping everything in Zoe's lap then perching up on the edge of her desk. She looked very satisfied with herself. ''Nigel, the dear, generous boy, never asks any awkward questions. Just handed these over and said he hoped everything would work out for you. Actually, you're not the first female in crisis I've sent up there and they all spoke highly of the place afterward.''

''What's it like?'' Zoe asked.

''Never been myself. It isn't called Hideaway Beach for nothing, and peace and quiet is not my bag. Neither is the sun, sea and surf. I can't swim, for starters, and I burn like mad. Anyway, Nigel said to tell you the kitchen cupboards, freezer and wine rack are all stocked up and to help yourself. There's also a gas station and general store half a mile down the road which fortunately has a liquor license. It has practically everything you might need. Fresh bread every day, milk, cigarettes, chocolates, condoms.''

''Very funny, Fran,'' Zoe said dryly. ''I don't think condoms are going to be high on my shopping list.''

''Well, you never know. His only warning is for you to leave before three this afternoon as after that the traffic heading north on a Friday afternoon would give blood pressure to a corpse. And he suggests you get up very very early on the Monday morning rather than try to drive back on the Sunday evening, for the same reason. You do still have your car, don't you?''

''Well, yes, of course I do, but…''

''I know exactly what you're going to say. You

don't finish here 'til six at the earliest on a Friday afternoon, since you have a slave driver of a boss who never knows when to quit. But just this once, I'm going to give you an early mark, starting right now. After all, we females should stick together. Can't have the males of the species thinking they have us taped, can we?''

Zoe didn't know what to say.

''No need to thank me,'' Fran said, laughing at her girl Friday's dumbfoundedness. ''I'll work your butt off next week to make up for it.''

Zoe smiled wryly. She didn't doubt it. Her boss was a workaholic if ever there was one. ''If Drake rings here or contacts you, you won't tell him where I am, will you?''

''I'll just say you asked for the afternoon off, you've gone away for the weekend but I don't know where. Now don't forget to turn your cell phone off as well. Or better yet, don't take it with you.''

''I always take it in the car with me for safety reasons and emergencies. But I'll definitely leave it turned off all weekend.''

''Excellent.''

When Zoe stood up with the map and the keys in hand, she was struck with a moment's doubt. ''Are you sure this is the right thing to do? Maybe Drake will get angry and dump *me*.''

''If he does, then he doesn't really love you, does he?''

''You're right.''

''Off you go now. And have fun.''

Zoe didn't think that was likely. But she smiled. ''Thanks again, Fran.''

Fran smiled back. ''My pleasure.''

3

MELINDA was home when Zoe let herself into the apartment. Not an unusual occurrence, even at two on a Friday afternoon.

Melinda was what was often cattily termed a rich bitch. But that wasn't strictly true. Sure, her father had given her this fully furnished two-bedroom apartment for her twenty-first birthday a couple of years back, but it was no palace, or penthouse.

It was, however, near new, with plush gray carpet, white walls and the sort of sleek modern clean-lined furniture which Zoe loved, so different from the clunky heavy wooden furniture filling the farmhouse back home.

Actually, on the market today, Melinda's place would have sold for close to half a million. No doubt about that. Even the grottiest apartment in Milson's Point was worth a packet.

Melinda was a very lucky girl to have received such an expensive present. Unfortunately, despite her darling daddy being a racehorse-owning billionaire, the day Melinda received the keys to the apartment, her allowance had been cut off.

"I've given you a roof over your head and that's all I'm going to do from now on," her father had bluntly announced at the time. ''If you want to feed and clothe yourself in future you'll have to get a job. Your brother had to make good on his own after twenty-one. I see no reason why you shouldn't do the same, just because you're female. You girls wanted equality. Well, now you've got it!''

Despite not having any practice at the art of supporting herself—she had done absolutely nothing since leaving school except socialize and shop—Melinda had risen to the challenge with gusto. First, she'd rented out the other bedroom in the apartment—Zoe was not Melinda's first roommate—then set about finding work as a model. She wasn't really qualified for anything else, and had no intention of serving in a store or working as a waitress. She wasn't tall enough for catwalk modeling at only five-eight, but her long blond hair, sultry face and cup-C breasts gave her plenty of work doing photographic modeling for fashion catalogs, especially those of the lingerie variety.

Modeling, however, was just a stopgap. Her ultimate ambition was to marry someone far richer than her father.

But not for some years yet. At twenty-three, Melinda was concentrating on having fun.

And have fun Melinda did! Although Melinda had a steady boyfriend named Ron, she also went out a lot without him. Parties. Premieres. Gallery openings. The races. You name it, if she was asked, Melinda went. And with her looks and social contacts, she received a lot of invitations.

Zoe found her a delightful roommate. Always

bright and cheery, and not at all lazy around the place. Which was a surprise, since Melinda had obviously been spoiled rotten as a child. But she liked and valued beautiful things and treated her own little home and her possessions with great respect. Open her closet or drawers any day, and all her lovely things would not only be beautifully arranged, but spotlessly clean. As was the apartment. She never dropped her clothes on the floor, or left dirty crockery around.

Best of all, Melinda didn't smoke. A rare breed, Zoe had found after sharing places with various other girls over the last few years. Most of them smoked like chimneys. It was so pleasant to come home to nice-smelling rooms, even when all the windows had been shut all day.

When Zoe walked in, Melinda was perched up on one of the white kitchen stools, carefully painting her fingernails at the black granite breakfast bar. She was dressed in traffic-stopping short-shorts and a cropped top, both blue. Melinda just loved blue in clothes. And why not? The color suited her blond hair and blue eyes.

"Good grief!" she exclaimed when she saw Zoe. "Have I lost track of time? Don't tell me it's gone six. Ron's picking me up at seven and I've only just started getting ready!"

"Don't panic. It's only twenty past two."

"Thank God. But that's silly daylight-saving time for you! You never know what time it is by looking out the window. So what are you doing home? You can't be sick. You never get sick. You're not sick, are you?" she asked, peering more closely at Zoe whilst she flicked her nails dry. ''You do look a bit stressed.''

''No. I'm not sick. Fran gave me an early mark.''

''You're kidding me. Commandante Phillips let you come home early and you're not even sick!''

''Nope.'' Zoe walked over, dumped her bag on the counter and switched on the electric jug.

Melinda eyed her warily. ''This is very strange. So what's up? Was there a bomb scare at the office? Some disgruntled husband whom your boss screwed over in court?''

''Nothing like that.''

''Then what? The mind boggles over what earth-shattering catastrophe could have led to such an unlikely occurrence.''

''Come now, Mel, Fran's not that bad. She's just a hard worker.''

''She works *you* hard. That I know.''

''But she appreciates the job I do, and she pays me well.''

''Huh.''

''You just don't like her, do you? Yet you've only met her once.''

''Once was enough. That woman is tough as an old boot. Maybe that's what's needed to be a top divorce lawyer these days, but I sure as heck wouldn't want to be married to her.''

Although Zoe thought Melinda was being a bit harsh, her comments brought home the fact that perhaps Fran hadn't been the best person to go to for advice over her dilemma with Drake. Fran was pretty cynical when it came to her views on life, men and sex. She'd accused Zoe of being a romantic idealist, but Zoe didn't think it was unreasonable to expect the man you loved and who said he loved you, to be faithful.

"For pity's sake, are you going to tell me why you're home early," Melinda burst out impatiently, "or are you just going to stand there for the rest of the day, staring into space?"

"I don't have much time," Zoe said, popping two slices of bread into the toaster. "I have to be packed and gone by three and I'm in desperate need of some food first."

"Packed? Gone by three? This is getting curiouser and curiouser."

"If you want to know all the grisly details, then don't interrupt," Zoe warned, already sensing that Melinda wasn't the right person to ask for advice, either. She just didn't take life and love seriously enough.

Melinda's big blue eyes rounded with even more gleeful curiosity. "Grisly details! Oooh. Do tell. Sorry," she said swiftly when Zoe threw her a baleful glance. "I won't say another word."

And she made a zipping gesture across her mouth.

Zoe rolled her eyes at her friend's pitiful attempt at a chastened face. This was going to be a total waste of time, but Melinda wouldn't give her any peace 'til she knew the ins and outs of everything. Just like June at work. And Betty back home.

Zoe supposed most women had a natural affinity for talking and gossiping. But she didn't. She'd always been more of a thinker than a talker. An introvert, as opposed to Melinda's extrovert nature. The good communication and social skills she now possessed hadn't come naturally. They'd been acquired. With a lot of practice and hard work. By nature, she was quite shy. And private. And particularly possessive about her innermost feelings.

Sometimes, Zoe felt that the person she now projected wasn't the real Zoe at all. Occasionally, when she looked in the mirror, she still saw the fat, shy tongue-tied teenager she'd once been.

"Zoe, for pity's sake!"

"Yes, yes, I'm just wondering where to start."

"Anywhere will do. Just *start!*"

Telling Melinda all the gory details took Zoe less time than it had to tell Fran, possibly because she wasn't sobbing hysterically anymore. Frankly, her overriding emotion now was just plain anger.

"I don't believe it," Melinda blurted out when Zoe had finally finished the sordid tale. "Drake cheated on you with some blond piece, just because she had a 'Baywatch' bustline? That doesn't make sense. I mean, not once, in all the times he's come here, has he ever given *me* the eye. And *I'm* a crash-hot-looking blonde with very nice boobs."

Zoe smiled a wry smile. Melinda never let modesty get in the way of self-praise.

"Let's not forget Drake has actually confessed here, Mel," Zoe reminded her ruefully. "But of course, it was only *just sex,*" she added with extra tartness. "And the woman threw herself at him. Practically tore off the poor darling's clothes. He was feeling like a bit of action and he couldn't help himself. She meant nothing to him at all.''

''Well, I could have told you that. Drake's crazy about *you.*''

''So he keeps telling me. But explain it to me, Mel. I mean, have *you* ever met some guy when you were crazy about someone else, but fancied this new guy so much that you just had to go to bed with him right away?''

''But of course! When I met Ron I was going out with Wayne who was a right hunk, I can tell you. But once I met Ron, I dropped Wayne like a shot.''

Zoe rolled her eyes. ''Yes, but you weren't in love with this Wayne, were you?''

Melinda shrugged. ''I guess not. Which is just as well,'' she added with a wicked grin. ''Because Ron's much better in the sack.''

''Oh, you're hopeless. You never take anything seriously.''

''And you, Zoe Simons, take life much too seriously. Look, for what it's worth, I agree with your boss for once. I think you should forgive Drake. Give him another chance. It's not as though he kept on with the blonde after he came back from the conference, did he? And she must live in Sydney to show up at the Rockery.''

Zoe took a bite of her toast, munching it thoughtfully before swallowing. ''No, I don't think she comes from Sydney. Drake was far too shocked at seeing her. I think she might have just been here for a visit. That old chap she was with could have been her father.''

''Okay, dump him then. Whatever makes you happy.''

''But that won't make me happy, will it? I'm going to be utterly wretched and lonely without him.''

''Rubbish! You're one hot-looking babe. You'll find another guy in no time, especially if you start coming places with me. You'll have so many gorgeous men hitting on you, you won't know which one to date first.''

''But I don't want to date some other guy,'' Zoe said frustratedly. ''And I don't care how gorgeous he is! I just want things the way they were. With Drake.''

Melinda sighed an exasperated sigh. ''Okay, give him another chance, then. But if you're going to do that, then what's the point of going away all by yourself up to some remote beach for the weekend? You might as well stay here, tell Loverboy you forgive him when he shows up tonight, then spend all weekend in the sack making up.''

Zoe cringed at the thought. How could she possibly go to bed with Drake with the image of him and that blonde doing it in an elevator still so clear in her head? ''I can't do that,'' she said, shuddering. ''Not this soon. Besides, Drake doesn't deserve to be forgiven that quickly. He deserves to suffer.''

Melinda frowned at her. ''That doesn't sound like you, Zoe. That sounds more like your boss. She'd be right into suffering. Bet she and her lawyer hubbie are into S & M in private. You know, bondage and black leather and stuff. But he'd be the one tied up and she'd have the whip. You could count on that.''

Zoe stared at her roommate, shocked. "Don't be silly. Normal people don't do things like that."

"Don't you believe it. Lots of normal-looking people are right into S & M. Or some form of it. Hasn't Drake ever wanted to tie you up?"

"Of course not!" The very idea! She'd had enough trouble just getting naked with him. The prospect of being naked and tied up sent a shudder of revulsion all through her, especially the thought of Drake looking at places she couldn't bear the thought of him looking at without her being able to move or cover herself up.

"Ron's always wanting to tie me up," Melinda confided blithely. "I might let him one day."

"Are you crazy? What if he…you know…did things you didn't want him to do?"

Melinda pulled a face. "Yeah, you're right. You'd have to trust a guy a hell of a lot to let him tie you up. And I'm not sure I trust Ron enough for that yet. I think I'll tie him up instead," she said, grinning. "Now *that* would be almost as much fun."

Zoe shook her head. "You're mad."

"Mad and bad," Melinda joked. "You should take lessons. Now, if it was *me* going away for the weekend after my boyfriend screwed some other female, I wouldn't be going to some lonely old beach shack. I'd be heading for some swinging resort and looking for a bit of action myself. Yep, I'd be giving ole Drakey boy a bit of his own medicine. That's what I'd be doing."

"But I'm not you, am I?" Zoe said, almost wishing

that she was. It must be great not to feel things so deeply for once.

''Which is just as well,'' Melinda countered, ''or I wouldn't like you as much as I do. Look, don't take any notice of me, Zoe,'' she went on, her smile fading abruptly. ''I can be a vicious bitch sometimes. Why do you think I want to marry a man richer than my father? Because I want to show that old tightwad a thing or two. I'll never forgive him for tossing me to the wolves like he did. If he'd wanted me to be a career girl from the word go, then why ever didn't he say so when I was still at school? Then I could have made something of myself while I had the chance. I wouldn't have to make a living being a clotheshorse and putting up with men's preconceptions of me, simply because I'm an underwear model!''

Zoe stared at her friend, amazed by the wealth of very real feeling behind her outburst. She hadn't realized Melinda's father had hurt her so much over what he did.

''Sorry,'' Melinda muttered. ''You have enough problems of your own without my going off.''

''I...I didn't realize you felt that way about your job. And I didn't know men treated you badly because you were a model.''

Melinda shrugged. ''Mostly they don't. But I met this pathetic example of the opposite sex today when I was on a shoot and he ignored me. Treated me like I was a nobody. Yet I was standing in front of him in the sexiest black lace underwear you've ever seen.''

''Who was he?''

''Some self-made upstart of a millionaire who's buying the fashion magazine I was doing the shoot for. Brother, did he think he was somebody. But my father could buy him ten times over!''

''Good-looking?''

''Yeah, I guess he was. He has the blackest of eyes and the longest eyelashes. And a great body for someone over thirty. But he was so arrogant.''

Zoe smiled. ''You were attracted to him.''

''I was not!''

''Yes, you were. And your nose was put out of joint because he didn't seem to want you.''

''Well...maybe a bit...''

''Will you be seeing him again?''

''I doubt it.''

''Will you be doing any more shoots for that magazine in the near future?''

''Next week. My agent rang me about it today. Some other girl was supposed to do it but she rang in sick and the magazine asked for me to replace her.''

''What a coincidence.''

Melinda frowned at Zoe's tone. ''You don't think...''

''It's possible, isn't it?'' Zoe said with a shrug. ''Let's face it, most men would at least *look* at you, Mel. Especially half-naked. The fact this chap ignored you says one of two things to me. He's either gay, or he does secretly fancy you, but he doesn't want to be obvious.''

''Good grief!'' Melinda exclaimed. ''Do you always think this deviously?''

''I didn't once,'' Zoe said dryly. ''But my experience with men is beginning to make me think outside the envelope. Now I really must get going or I'll hit the traffic. If and when Drake calls, tell him I've gone away for the weekend but you don't know where.''

''He's not going to be happy.''

''Too bad. I wasn't happy today.''

''Oooh. Them's fightin' words.''

''I'm in a fightin' mood. Which is why I'm going away. I need time to think. And time to calm down. Maybe by Monday, I'll see things a little clearer.''

''Nothing in relationships with men is ever clear, Zoe,'' Melinda said. ''They're a breed unto themselves. Impossible to really understand what makes their peculiar male minds tick. It's a case of can't live with them, can't live without them.''

''Oh, I can live without them,'' Zoe said. ''I've done it before and I can do it again. I just have to work out if I want to.''

4

ZOE didn't have to consult Nigel's map for the first part of her drive north. She knew the way to Port Stephens. When she'd first bought her much-loved car a year ago, she'd spent every weekend going for long drives and investigating all the seaside towns within a half-day distance of Sydney.

Zoe had a secret passion for trips to the beach, perhaps because she'd rarely gone to the seaside during her growing-up years. The children of dairy farmers learned young that you can never go far from home, or for long. Having to milk the cows morning and afternoon tied you to the place, good and proper.

Unfortunately, Zoe soon found that going away by yourself for the weekend wasn't all that much fun. It was reasonably pleasurable during the day, sightseeing or strolling along a beach, but when the day ended and she returned to her motel room all alone, her mood would change.

Eating alone in restaurants was the worst. And watching other couples, holding hands across candlelit tables. She discovered there was nothing worse than not having anyone to talk to and share your experiences with. When her solitary excursions began to seriously depress her, she stopped.

Which made her wonder why on earth she'd agreed to this silly idea of going away for the weekend on her own this time. She would have far too much time to think and brood. She would have been better off staying home and sorting things out with Drake, one way or another.

Zoe sighed in disgruntlement. It was too late now. She was almost at Port Stephens. Which meant it was time to pull over to the side of the highway and consult Nigel's map in more detail before she missed the turning to Hideaway Beach.

Five minutes later she was safely on the side road leading to her destination. It was narrow and winding, with nothing on either side but the kind of low trees and rather unattractive scrub one found when you were this close to the sea. The soil was mostly sand and just didn't grow lush green grass or nice tall trees. There were no houses, either, which meant it was probably a state reserve.

Zoe felt she'd been driving for ages by the time the gas station came into view on her left. It was ancient, as was the general store attached, but surprisingly well stocked, with a cheerful old guy behind the counter who liked to chat.

It was just after six by the time Zoe was on her way again with her passenger seat carrying a bag full of fresh bread, milk, eggs, two wickedly fattening bars of chocolate and a couple of her favorite magazines. She hadn't thought to throw in a book to read before leaving home and didn't trust the likes of Nigel Cox to have anything on his bookshelves she might enjoy.

Frankly, she hadn't thought about this trip enough at all, she now conceded. She hadn't even bothered to change clothes before leaving. Just chucked a few items in an overnight bag and got going.

It wasn't like her to act so hastily. The drama with Drake had tipped her world upside down, and her with it.

Zoe rounded a long sweeping curve and there, straight ahead, lay the horizon of the Pacific Ocean, big and vast and blue. Her heart lifted at the sight, and she was suddenly glad she'd come, if for nothing else than this moment.

But the moment was gone all too quickly, cold, hard reality returning to darken her own personal horizon. This weekend escape was not going to solve anything. She was just delaying the difficult decision over what she should do. Forgive and forget? Or dump Drake and try to move on...

The car slowed to a crawl as Zoe's mind drifted once more. It was all very well for Mel to say she'd find someone else in no time. Zoe had never been the sort of girl to pick up men easily, even now, when her looks were no longer a drawback. Men often found her standoffish. Some had even called her stuck-up.

But she wasn't. Not at all. She was just reserved. And naturally wary. She didn't warm to strangers easily. She was slow to give affection and friendship, and even slower to accept it from others. Which made her instant liking of Melinda, for instance, most unusual. She hadn't even really liked Drake at first meeting. He'd impressed her, yes. But liked?

No…not exactly. She'd thought him a little pushy. But she'd found his dogged pursuit of her very flattering, and very seductive. There'd been the flowers twice a week. Phone calls every day. Presents. Poetry, even.

How could she help falling in love with him in the end? Or going to bed with him? Or being devastated by his cheating on her? He'd made her think she was his entire world, and vice versa.

The sound of a horn honking loudly made Zoe jump in her seat, her eyes flying to the rear-vision mirror. A bright yellow truck was right behind her, several surf boards strapped to the roof. The male driver was making an impatient left-handed motion with his hand.

Zoe hadn't realized she'd been stopped, smack-dab in the middle of the road. Embarrassed, she smiled an apology at the driver in the rear-vision mirror. After a moment's hesitation he smiled back, and the oddest little quiver ran through Zoe from top to toe.

It shocked her so much that she stared at his reflection for a few seconds before moving her car over to the left, carrying with her the image of the bronze-skinned, blond-haired, broad-shouldered hunk wearing wrap-around sunglasses and the brightest orange T-shirt she'd ever seen. His sun-streaked hair was short and spiked, and his face had that chiseled structure which you saw a lot on male models, his lantern jawline covered with a few days' stubble. Naturally, in those sunglasses, she couldn't see the color of his eyes, but she guessed they would be blue.

This last train of thought startled Zoe. What on

earth was she doing, speculating over what color eyes he had? But even as she reprimanded herself for such silly nonsense, he was driving by and peering at her through their respective side windows. Her heart began to race and she started wondering if *he* was speculating on the color of *her* eyes, which were similarly masked by sunglasses. Her hand lifted and she almost took them off, wanting him to see that her own were big and brown and long-lashed.

They were her best feature, her eyes.

But she caught herself just in time and the moment of madness passed, as did the truck. Thank goodness.

What had she thought she was doing?

A minute before she'd been agonizing over how devastated she was by Drake's cheating on her. Then the next moment, there *she* was, almost flirting with some stranger.

There was absolutely no excuse for such behavior, no matter how sexy the guy in the truck was.

Sexy?

How could she possibly tell if he was sexy from a couple of brief passing glances? She hadn't even seen all of him. For all she knew, he could have beady little eyes, a big blubbery butt and the personality of a store mannequin.

Oh, yeah, scorned some new inner voice which Zoe had never been tuned into before. *Who do you think you're kidding, honey? He's going to have beautiful blue eyes, tight buns, and the charm of the devil.*

Zoe groaned. This was crazy and so unlike herself. There again, today hadn't exactly been like any other day. She'd been brought face-to-face with her boyfriend's raunchy new friend; quizzed by her boss on intimate sexual matters; then been told by her roommate that she shouldn't be slinking off by herself. She should be throwing herself into a fun fling out of revenge.

Was that what this was? Her subconscious wanting to punish Drake by flirting with another man? Her own shaky self-esteem, perhaps, looking for reassurance that she *was* attractive?

She sincerely hoped so. She didn't want it to be that other sordid scenario Fran had described of being struck by instant lust for some good-looking stranger and wanting nothing from him but down-and-dirty sex.

No, no, it couldn't be that. She didn't want to even consider the possibility. But even as she dismissed the idea, Zoe sincerely hoped she wouldn't run into the man in the truck again.

When she looked up, his yellow vehicle had reached the end of the road and was turning right. Within seconds, it had disappeared from view.

Zoe sat up straight, her stomach crunching down hard.

Right. He'd turned *right.*

She snatched up Nigel's second map and studied its very detailed drawing of Hideaway Beach's layout.

Her heart rate accelerated as her eyes confirmed what she'd remembered from her earlier perusal. The beach was U-shaped, with rugged peninsulas stretching out into the ocean at each end. Sand dunes rose behind the main stretch of beach, on top of which sat a long, face-the-ocean visitors' car lot. The half dozen or so weekenders which Hideaway Beach boasted were grouped together down the southerly end, their fronts facing northeast. A short dead-end road led 'round to the back of them, a road which required a right-hand turn at the end of this road.

If you were a surfer just come for the waves, you would go straight ahead and park in the visitors' car lot, not turn right as the truck had done.

There was only one logical conclusion. The hunk in the truck either lived here, or was staying here on vacation. If that was the case, she was likely to run into him again at some stage this weekend.

Zoe groaned her frustration. She'd come up here to sort out her feelings about men and sex, not have them confused further.

Irritated beyond words, she switched on the engine, checked there was no car coming, then drove down to the end of the road where she stopped for a few seconds and scanned the vehicles in the visitors' car lot.

The yellow truck wasn't among them.

Zoe hadn't expected it to be.

Sighing her resignation to the fact Mr. Orange T-shirt wasn't a visitor, she steered her small silver sedan onto the dirt track on her right and drove slowly along its pot-holed surface, glancing over to her left every now and then.

Hideaway Beach was certainly very beautiful. But very quiet. Only half a dozen people on the sand. A couple more swimming in the almost-flat waters. There wasn't a single board rider out in the water, which was understandable considering the absence of decent waves. There was no sign of Mr. Orange T-shirt anywhere.

Zoe was annoyed with herself for even looking.

Resolving to banish him from her mind once and for all, she swung her eyes back onto the road ahead and concentrated on finding Nigel's place, which, according to his map, was the second house she'd come to on her left, a white weatherboard cottage with a gray colorbond roof.

Actually, from the road, all Zoe could see of the weekenders were the roofs below her. The first one had an unusual-colored roof. Royal-blue. Zoe had never seen a roof that color before, but she rather liked it.

The gray colorbond roof of Nigel's place came into view a short way after the bright blue, and Zoe began looking for the driveway.

There was a small, white-painted mailbox on the side of the road, but no sign of a driveway. Zoe parked on the grass verge just beyond the mailbox then climbed out to check out what was what.

Nigel's weekender looked very cute and cozy down below her, its back steps tucked in to the hillside, with the beach less than fifty feet from the front porch. There *was* a footpath of sorts leading from the mailbox down to the back door, but absolutely no way of getting her car any closer than where she was. The intervening ground was too steep and too rough.

There was nothing for it but to carry everything down that hazardous-looking path. Zoe glanced over at the weekenders on her left and right, telling herself she wasn't looking for a sign of Mr. Orange T-shirt, even though she was.

The place on her right looked deserted, with no vehicle anywhere. The one on her left with the bright-blue roof was lucky enough to have a driveway leading to what looked like a carport on the other side of the house, but she couldn't see enough of it to make out any vehicles parked there.

Still, it would be just like Mr. Orange T-shirt to live in a house with a royal-blue roof, sky-blue walls and wraparound porches painted a dark rich red. And it would be just like her luck today to have him as a neighbor for the whole weekend.

Shaking her head, Zoe returned to the car, collected her various bags and set off down the pathway. She was halfway down the roughly hewn steps when something orange caught the corner of her left eye and her head jerked in that direction.

Big mistake. She should have kept watching where she was going, especially since she was wearing high heels. The second she took her eyes off the uneven steps, she misjudged a distance, one of her high heels caught against something and she lurched forward. In joggers or bare feet Zoe might have been able to regain her balance. As it was, she whirled with the bags in her hands in the air, and for one adrenaline-charged moment, she thought she could save herself.

But her center of gravity could not be righted and all was finally lost, Zoe tipping full front-forward. With a loud yelp she instinctively brought her hands up to save her face, and the bags came with her.

Just as well. For they cushioned her fall and possibly prevented her breaking an arm, or a leg. She still landed heavily, her knees getting the worst of it as she slid down a couple of steps further before coming to an ungainly halt.

She was still sprawled on the ground, totally winded, when a pair of strong arms slid around her waist.

''Are you all right?'' a male voice asked as he hoisted her up onto her feet.

Zoe saw the orange T-shirt first and groaned silently. It would be him, wouldn't it? Fate was being very cruel to her today.

''Yes, I…I think so,'' she said, delaying looking up at him by dusting down her dress. But good manners finally forced her to glance up at her gallant Good Samaritan and say a proper thank-you.

She had to look up a good way, he was so tall. Taller than she'd imagined. And even more handsome, with a strong straight nose, a cute dimple in his squared chin and a perfectly gorgeous mouth.

But it was his eyes which captivated her the most. They *were* blue, as blue and as deep as the ocean. Eyes to drown in.

Eyes to watch your own wide-eyed reflection in while he rocks back and forth above you, his beautiful body buried deep inside yours.

Did she gasp out loud in shocked horror?

She hoped not.

''You've gone very pale,'' he said, frowning. ''Are you sure you're all right? You're not going to faint, are you?''

"No," she choked out. "No, I don't think so." Though it was possible.

"Perhaps you'd better sit down for a few seconds, put your head down between your knees."

Another erotic scenario exploded into her mind, one in which it wasn't *her* head down between her knees.

Zoe swallowed a couple more times.

"No, no, I'm fine," she said at last in strangled tones, desperately trying to pull herself together. "But I've lost my sunglasses. Can you see my sunglasses? Oh, there they are." She swooped on them, and jammed them back on, hoping they hid her escalating panic.

"You've ruined your panty hose," he pointed out.

Her eyes dropped to her legs, then shifted over to *his* legs, which were well on display, his colorful board shorts not covering up much.

They were the best-shaped legs on a man she'd ever seen. Totally tanned, long and very strong, with great thighs.

Well able to support you when he hikes you up onto his hips and then…

"Serves me right for being silly enough to be wearing high heels," she blurted out. "It's just that I drove straight up here from work. Didn't really have time to change. I just threw a few things together and jumped in the car. My main concern was missing the Friday traffic heading north out of Sydney. But not to worry. I doubt I'll be needing panty hose up here this weekend anyway."

She was prattling on like a fool. But anything was

better than conjuring up more appalling scenarios involving them both.

"I think your eggs might have seen better days as well," he said dryly, and Zoe looked blank.

"Eggs," he repeated, indicating her groceries which had scattered all over the place. The half-dozen eggs, which had been carefully placed at the top of the bag, had spilled from their carton, all of them broken.

"Oh, dear..." Zoe sighed, suddenly feeling very tired.

"I could go buy you some more, if you like," he offered.

She stared at him. When guys started offering to go out of their way for you, it usually meant they fancied you. The thought that Mr. Orange T-shirt might be as attracted to her as she was to him, produced a mad mixture of guilty pleasure and even more outrageous thoughts.

Yes, go get me some more eggs, you gorgeous darling sexy man. And a dozen condoms whilst you're at it.

Zoe was infinitely relieved she was wearing sunglasses, for surely the wickedness of her thoughts must be reflected in her eyes.

"Thank you but no," she said stiffly. "I can manage without the eggs. But it was very nice of you to offer."

"No sweat." He immediately hunkered down and began putting her groceries back into the bag.

Impossible not to notice in that position that he

didn't have a big blubbery butt. His buns *were* as trim and taut as she'd feared they would be.

Afraid that any further ogling of his perfect butt would conjure up yet another wicked fantasy, Zoe wrenched her eyes away and hurried to pick up her handbag. But when she moved toward where her overnight bag had fallen, her gallant knight to the rescue was there before her, scooping it up first.

"I think I'd better carry these the rest of the way down for you. You're still wearing those very nice but potentially lethal high heels," he added with a wry little smile.

"Please don't bother."

"It's no bother. I presume you're staying at Nigel's place down there?"

"Well...yes. You know Nigel, do you?"

"Pretty well."

"Oh? How well?" She didn't realize 'til the words were out of her mouth how they might sound. The thought that this fellow might be gay hadn't even crossed her mind.

He laughed, his blue eyes sparkling with genuine good humor. "Not *that* well. But we have a drink together sometimes when he's up here. I live over there." And he nodded toward the house with the royal-blue roof. "For the moment, that is," he added. "The owner's letting me stay while I do some renovating work for him."

"It's a very colorful house."

"Yes. He likes bright colors. So what about you? Are you a friend of our esteemed big-city lawyer? Or a client?"

Zoe felt she had to terminate this getting-to-know-you conversation fairly quickly, or risk giving her far too attractive neighbor the wrong idea. She could not even begin to speculate what she might do if he started coming on to her. The thought was far too perversely thrilling for words.

''No, I hardly know Mr. Cox at all, to be honest. But I...uh...'' She hesitated over revealing specific details of her life to a virtual stranger. ''I know one of his partners,'' she said, instead of saying she worked for Fran. ''She asked Nigel if I could borrow his place for the weekend. I...um...I needed to get away from Sydney for a couple of days.''

''Ah...life in the fast lane getting too much for you, was it?''

''Something like that.''

He nodded sagely and Zoe realized he was older than she'd first thought. Late twenties, perhaps. Maybe even thirty. ''I know exactly how you feel,'' he said ruefully. ''But a weekend away won't be much of a cure. You need longer than that.''

''Well, I have to be back at work on Monday, so one weekend is all I've got. Look, I don't mean to be rude, but I'm terribly hot and tired and in desperate need of a shower. If you'd just drop those things next to Nigel's back door, that would be great.''

''Okay,'' he agreed, but Zoe thought he looked a bit disappointed. Maybe he'd been hoping she'd invite him in for a drink, or something.

Or something morphed in her mind to a scene from a recent movie where the leading man and leading lady—within a few minutes of meeting—pounced on each other like wild beasts. Clothes were ripped off in seconds and absolutely nothing was left to the imagination as the hero, for want of a better word, proceeded to ravish the heroine up against a wall.

At the time, Zoe had thought the whole thing quite incredible, as well as supremely tacky.

She still thought such behavior tacky, but not quite so incredible.

She tried to imagine, as she followed her far too sexy neighbor down to the back door, what would happen if she did invite him in. Would he make a pass? And if he did, what would *she* do?

He placed her bags by the step, then turned to face her, his own expression thoughtful.

"The name's Aiden, by the way," he said. "And yours?"

"Zoe."

"Nice name. Well, Zoe, if you need anything over the next two days, just whistle. I'm always hereabouts. When I'm not off surfing somewhere, that is. I presume you know how to whistle?" he added, throwing a provocative little smile over his shoulder as he started to walk away. "Just put your very pretty lips together and blow."

He didn't look back again as his long legs carried him swiftly away. Which was just as well, because what Zoe's sexually charged mind was doing to his parting words made her face go a brighter red than his porch.

5

WITHIN a minute of returning to his place, Aiden was stretched out in a chair on the front porch, drinking a beer and doing his best not to think about the girl in the house next door having a shower.

A futile exercise. He'd been thinking about her nonstop since she'd smiled at him in her rear-vision mirror and charged up every testosterone-based cell he owned.

Playing knight to the rescue just now had only confirmed what he already knew. That she was big trouble, both to his peace of mind *and* body.

Aiden gulped another mouthful of beer, then sighed.

Six months he'd lasted here at Hideaway Beach without so much as a single bad night's sleep. Six months of wonderfully uncomplicated celibacy.

His life was blessedly simple. He surfed first thing in the morning, and again, late in the afternoon, spending the hours in between doing up the once-ramshackle beachhouse he'd bought a few months earlier. After dinner—which he usually cooked himself—his evenings were spent reading, or listening to music. He didn't have a television and never bought newspapers. If he felt the need for human conversation, he chatted to other surfers, or the local fishermen, or to his mom over the phone. Occasionally, when Nigel was up for the weekend, he went over to his place for dinner and a bottle of good wine.

But he rarely stayed long. He didn't want to be contaminated by listening to Nigel's complaints about his clients and his lovers. He certainly *never* wanted to reminisce on the time *he'd* been a client.

Aiden was well aware his sabbatical from real life would come to an end one day, but only when *he* decided and not before. He wanted to keep the world outside at a distance for a while longer. He certainly didn't want to be attracted to some mixed-up, auburn-haired city chick who was obviously in the middle of a personal crisis which had necessitated her coming up here to Hideaway Beach for a break.

He didn't want to speculate on whether she was in the throes of a divorce, or a palimony suit, or a sexual harassment case, or any of the multiple reasons why women hired lawyers like Fran Phillips, who then took the poor husband or boyfriend or boss to court and screwed them over for everything they were worth, both financially and emotionally.

Aiden checked himself with a frown. Brother, that sounded really bitter. And he wasn't bitter anymore. If anything, Marci had done him a favor, suing him. She'd made him see the emptiness of seeking nothing but superficial success and material wealth; forced him to reevaluate what he really wanted in life.

And when he finally found out what that was—he'd been searching for it in his head for six months now—he'd go after it.

Until that happened, the last thing he wanted was to get back on the sexual merry-go-round. Going to bed with the delectable but obviously distressed Zoe was not a good idea, no matter how much he found her attractive.

The trouble was she wanted him, too. He could tell.

But she didn't *want* to want him. That he could tell as well.

Which was the most bewildering aspect of this whole situation.

Aiden had never come across a female before who wanted him, and had resisted him. If anything, they'd always thrown themselves at him, or at least made him aware they were available, if and when he wanted them. Such was the powerful combination of heaven-sent looks and man-made money.

There again, Zoe didn't know he had money, did she?

Clearly, she hadn't recognized him.

Aiden frowned. Maybe she was the sort of girl who only surrendered to a physical attraction if the man was wealthy or famous? Such females did exist, he knew only too well. Yet somehow he didn't think Zoe was of that ilk. She'd been too sweetly flustered by everything just now to be of the cold-blooded, gold-digging variety.

Why, he wondered for the umpteenth time, had she sent him away just now, instead of inviting him in as most women would have done?

There were only a couple of answers which didn't bruise his male ego. Perhaps she'd sworn off all men for a while, as he had women. Or perhaps she'd been badly hurt by some sleazy guy and no longer trusted the opposite sex. He could identify with that as well. Lack of trust was the reason why he'd lied to her about owning this house.

Another futile gesture, since Zoe clearly wasn't going to come across. But at that moment he'd been hoping she might, and he'd egotistically and rather romantically hankered for her to come to his bed because she wanted Aiden the man, not Aiden, one-time world surfing champion, or Aiden the millionaire owner of the Aus-Surf chain.

Thinking of her in his bed brought his mind back to her very beddable body with its pretty breasts, tiny waist and deliciously rounded derriere. He'd had a good look at *that* when she'd been sprawled facedown on the ground, with her skirt flipped up to her waist.

Aiden had always been a butt man.

And a breast man, he conceded with a wry laugh.

And a leg man.

Hell, he liked every bit of a woman. Their shape. Their smell. Their softness.

His groan carried intense frustration. Whatever had possessed him to give them up? If he hadn't, he wouldn't be here now, with a hard-on the size of the Centrepoint Tower. He must have been mad!

Sculling the rest of the beer, Aiden went inside to get another can. Then another. Then yet another. Dinner that evening was a liquid one. As was dessert.

Aiden was to find, however, that getting drunk was a poor substitute for getting laid. His revved-up hormones still had him tossing and turning for most of the night. Sleep finally came around three, but when he woke, nothing had changed, a fact confirmed by the ready-to-fire state of his sexual equipment.

Aiden shook his head irritably and did the only thing a man of his nature could do. He went for a very long, very cold, early-morning swim.

Then started planning a seduction.

THE brass bed was big, and soft. Very soft. So were the silk scarves which bound her to the bedposts. They didn't hurt at all, not even when she writhed and wriggled.

And she writhed and wriggled a lot, gasping and moaning as her dream lover did things to her with his hands and mouth. Exciting things. Delicious things. Wicked things.

She was naked, of course. Naked and exposed and unable to stop him looking at her and touching her at will. Kissing all her intimate places. Sucking at her nipples. Invading her with his tongue.

But there was no embarrassment. Only pleasure. The most mind-bending pleasure. Sweet and dark and decadent.

Yes, yes, lick me there. Suck it. No, bite it.

She moaned when he did, her head twisting from side to side. If only she could see him. If only he'd take off the other scarf which covered her eyes.

''Who are you?'' she asked, though she already suspected. Who else did she know who smelled of sea salt?

''No talking,'' he replied in a very familiar voice. ''If you talk, you'll wake up. And you don't want that, do you?''

She shuddered at the thought. No, no. Not yet. Please not yet.

"I...I just want to see you."

"That's not what you want," he murmured as his hands ran lightly up over her body, across her tensely held stomach, her stiffened nipples, her stretched-up arms.

"This is what you want," he said, and suddenly, he was there, between her legs, filling her, thrilling her.

"Yes," she agreed, her body quivering.

Her climax was but a heartbeat away when her eyelids shot upward like a blind on a window, sunlight spearing her pupils.

Zoe sat bolt upright, blinking, gasping.

It took several seconds for her ragged breathing to calm, and cold hard reality to return.

There was no brass bed. No scarves. No Aiden.

A dream. It had all been a dream.

Zoe groaned. She supposed she should have been relieved that she wasn't really tied, naked, to a bed. But all she felt was disappointment. As much as Zoe knew she'd never enjoy such activities in real life—she'd never be that uninhibited, for starters—it was still hard not to wish that the dream might have lasted just a little bit longer.

Sighing, Zoe glanced at her watch on the bedside table. Ten to eight. Not late. But the sun was already streaming into the bedroom, promising another hot day.

Get up, she told herself. Have a shower. Make yourself some breakfast.

Dragging her body out of bed, she padded down the central corridor into the one and only bathroom. Fifteen minutes later, she emerged with her wet hair wrapped up in one of Nigel's plush navy towels, her steam-pinked body snugly encased in the matching navy bathrobe which had been hanging on the back of the bathroom door.

She was making her way back along the corridor to the kitchen to make breakfast when the doorbell rang.

Zoe halted at the sound, then peered down at the front door with its upper panel of frosted glass, through which she could see a tall, undoubtedly male silhouette.

''Oh, no, Drake,'' she groaned, and bolted back into the bathroom where she stared in horror at her reflection.

No one other than Mel had seen her totally without makeup in years. She needed makeup to cover the smattering of freckles across her nose and cheeks, and to transform the rest of her from a country hick into a city sophisticate. And she *really* needed her hair styled cleverly around her face to hide its round shape. With it bundled up under a towel and no makeup on, she looked about sixteen, a baby-faced sixteen.

Zoe would rather be dead than to let Drake see her this way. And who else could it be, knocking on the front door here at around eight in the morning?

Drake must have found out her whereabouts from Fran. There was no other answer.

And now here he was, on her doorstep.

Zoe didn't know whether to be flattered, or furious.

"Ahoy in there, Zoe," a male voice shouted through the door. "Don't panic now. It's just your friendly next-door neighbor with some eggs. I had a few to spare."

Zoe's mouth dropped open. It was Aiden. Not Drake.

Oh, my God…

"Just…just a moment," she called back, then went into a complete panic. Suddenly, she wished it *was* Drake at the door. Drake didn't make her mind go totally blank and her body begin to tremble uncontrollably.

Think, girl. Think! He hasn't come over here at this hour simply to give you eggs. You're not *that* naive. He's going to make some kind of pass.

Zoe's lack of makeup and grooming suddenly became a desirable asset. Aiden wouldn't think her so attractive this morning, with her freshly scrubbed face and no-hair look. As much as she hated showing herself like this to anyone, this situation called for drastic measures.

Zoe marched resolutely toward the door, resashing the robe around her waist more tightly on the way.

Unfortunately, this action reminded Zoe that she was naked underneath the robe, her tingling flesh still suffering from the after-effects of that incredible dream. Facing her fantasy lover was not going to be easy, but it had to be done.

Taking one last steadying breath, she pulled back the bolt and opened the front door.

The sight of Aiden standing there in nothing but a

tattered pair of denim shorts, shook Zoe considerably. Okay, so the day was hot. Even hotter than yesterday, but did he have to go around half naked?

Zoe did her best not to appear rattled, or to look at him with anything remotely like the disturbing feelings his near-nakedness evoked in her.

It wasn't desire. Desire was too tame a word for what she felt when she looked at this man.

Lust. That was what it was. Lust. The kind of lust Fran had talked about which didn't require niceties. Or even foreplay.

Her craving was strictly sexual. And incredibly basic. When she looked at Aiden's beautiful male body, all she could think of was how it would feel to touch him and kiss him, to have him on top of her, and inside her.

How she kept her expression as bland as she did, she would never know. Pride, she supposed.

"You're up early this morning," she said, trying to sound casual. But it was hard with him looking *her* over in such an open and admiring fashion. He didn't seem at all taken aback by her less than perfect appearance. In fact, if she wasn't mistaken, he seemed to prefer it.

Maybe he liked the casual, just-out-of-the-shower look. He certainly didn't believe in much grooming himself. He still hadn't shaved. And his hair was sticking up all over the place.

Yet for all that, he looked so sexy it was a crime.

"I'm up early every morning," he returned.

"So am I. Usually. But I slept in this morning."

He smiled. "I'm glad. Otherwise you'd have already had your breakfast. Here,'' he said, handing her a carton of half a dozen eggs. ''Enjoy.''

''You must let me pay you for them.''

''Not at all.''

''You're very kind.''

He smiled. ''Not *that* kind. I have an ulterior motive.''

''Oh?'' she said warily. Here it comes...

''I needed an excuse to come over and see you again.''

She stared at him, surprised by his blunt honesty, and terrified of what he was going to say next. Please don't, her eyes pleaded.

''I wondered if you'd like to come out to dinner with me tonight. There are plenty of good restaurants around and I do own some decent clothes. Not that you'd know by looking at me this morning,'' he added, grinning. ''I'll even promise to shave. So what about it?''

Her mouth went dry. Never had the devil tempted her so badly.

''I'm sorry,'' she said. ''But I...I can't.''

His eyes darkened in the way the sky does just before a storm. ''Can't, Zoe? Or won't?''

''Does it matter? The answer's the same.''

''It matters to me.''

''Won't, then.''

''Why?''

''I...I'm not free.''

His eyes dropped to her left hand. ''You're not wearing any rings,'' he stated bluntly.

"I didn't say I was married. I said I wasn't free to go out with you."

"Are you engaged, then?"

"No."

"Living with someone?"

"No."

"Then you're free in my books."

"But I'm not free in mine," she stated firmly. "I'm involved with someone. And I love him very much."

"But does *he* love *you* very much?" he countered.

Oh, why did she hesitate? "He...he says he does."

"Huh. If he loves you so much, then why has he let you come up here all by yourself? If you were my girlfriend, I wouldn't let you out of my sight."

She stiffened. "Well, I'm *not* your girlfriend and Drake doesn't *let* me do anything. Not that it's any of your business."

"I'm making it my business."

"Then that's very presumptuous of you," she snapped.

"Is he married?"

"No, he is not! Look, I think you should leave, if you're going to get personal and offensive."

He stared at her, clearly taken aback by her stand. His eyes searched her face, as though he could not believe what he was hearing.

"Just tell me one thing. Would you go out with me if this boyfriend of yours was out of the picture?"

She didn't say a word, but her eyes must have betrayed her.

"That's what I thought," he said, a little smugly. "You know, Zoe, you don't love this guy as much as you think you do. If you did, you wouldn't have looked at me like you did yesterday.''

A flustered heat started gathering in Zoe's face. ''Please go. And take your eggs with you.''

When she held them out, he shook his head. ''Keep them,'' he growled, and stalked off.

Zoe almost called him back. Almost. But in the end, decency won and the devil was defeated.

''Well done,'' Aiden muttered to himself as he marched back to his house. ''Very subtle. You'd give Casanova a run for his money with a technique like that.''

Clearly, six months' celibacy hadn't done much for his seduction skills. Or was it that he'd never had any in the first place?

The truth was sex had always come easy to Aiden, right from an early age. He'd never had to chase after it. Girls had always chased after him. At school, he'd always had the prettiest girls in class following him around like puppies. During his years on the world surfing circuit, there'd been gorgeous chicks by the bucket-load hanging around the tournaments. Surfing groupies, they were called. There was never a question of having to work too hard to have any one of them he wanted. He'd just have to give her the eye.

He hadn't bothered with a steady girlfriend back then. That kind of relationship wouldn't have fitted in with his lifestyle. For one thing, he'd needed to concentrate on his surfing. And then, there was the constant traveling.

Casual sex and a pocketful of condoms had been the order of the day. And most nights.

Later, however, after injury had forced him to retire from professional surfing, and he'd turned his ambitions elsewhere, Aiden had considered having a real relationship. He'd even started a couple. But they'd never worked out.

He hadn't been really in love, he supposed. Though he thought he was at the time. Not in love enough, however, for him to put his partner first, before his business. Both girls had complained of his lack of true commitment.

So he'd given up the idea of a steady girlfriend and gone back to dating different girls, if and when he felt the need for sex. He had little trouble finding "dates." Rich men rarely suffered the pangs of rejection. Aiden certainly hadn't had no said to him too often.

Zoe had said no to him today, however, and there was absolutely nothing Aiden could think of to do which would sway her mind. Unfortunately, she was a girl of strong character, and rather old-fashioned principle.

For once in his life, he hadn't got what he wanted, woman-wise, and it didn't sit well with him.

So he did the only thing a man of his nature could do.

He went surfing.

6

YOU did the right thing, Zoe praised herself after Aiden left. If you'd said yes, you'd have been no better than Drake. Now, make yourself some breakfast and stop worrying. Okay, so Aiden *did* seem a bit upset that you wouldn't go out with him. He'll get over it. It's not as though he's in love with you. He only wanted a dinner date, and then you for afters.

Zoe savoured the thought of being Aiden's after-dinner afters while she cooked and ate two of his eggs for breakfast. What would he be like as a real lover? she started wondering. What sort of things would he do?

''Oh, do stop thinking about that infernal man,'' Zoe muttered, and forcibly turned her mind to what she would actually *do* for the rest of the day.

Despite the heat, swimming was out, as was strolling along the water's edge. She wasn't going to do a single thing which might risk running into Aiden again. As much as Zoe had smugly congratulated herself on turning his invitation down, she wasn't sure if she would do so well on a second occasion.

Which meant outdoor pursuits here at Hideaway Beach were not on the agenda.

Really, there was nothing for it but to get out of

here. But not back to Sydney. Not yet. She was still very angry with Drake, and still not impressed with his "just sex" excuse. Maybe she understood it a bit better, after meeting Aiden, but if *she* could resist temptation, then why couldn't Drake have done the same? After all, on a scale of one to ten, she'd put the bottle blonde at around nine and Aiden at twenty-five! So whose temptation was worse?

All Zoe could think was that Drake's love for her couldn't be as strong as her love for him. Maybe Aiden had been right about that.

Thinking about Drake gave her a sudden thought and she went to check the message bank on her cell phone.

Nothing from Drake. Nothing at all.

Rather odd, came the caustic thought, if he loved her so much.

Zoe punched out her home number and Melinda answered after several rings.

"Hello," she grumped. Zoe's roommate was not a morning person.

"Hi, Mel, it's Zoe here."

"Oh, hi, Zoe," she said, attempting to brighten up. "What's up?"

"Nothing drastic. Did Drake call 'round before you went out last night?"

"Nope."

"Any message from him on the answering machine?"

"Nope."

"He didn't call my cell phone, either," Zoe said, biting her bottom lip.

Mel's sigh wafted down the line. ''Look, just dump the two-timing bastard and be done with it. Then you can go out and have the entire surf club up there at... Where is it you're staying?''

''Hideaway Beach. And there's no surf club here. It's a very small beach.''

''Pity. Some of those lifesaver types are real hunks. Nothing screwable at all around?''

Zoe stifled a groan. ''Can we get off the subject of sex?''

''If you insist. So when are you coming home? I'm lonely here without you.''

Zoe was touched. ''I'll probably get on the road first thing in the morning. Then I'll miss the Sunday afternoon traffic.''

''So what are you going to do today?''

''I thought I'd drive into Nelson Bay and do some window-shopping. Have a bite to eat. Maybe catch a movie.''

''Wow. Aren't you the wild one!''

Zoe laughed. ''I'm not a party animal like you.'' Except in my dreams!

''Maybe not, but you should learn to loosen up a bit, Zoe. There's more to life than working like a Trojan and always looking like you stepped out of a band box. So I repeat. Dump Drake and live a little.''

''Maybe he's already dumped me.''

''That might be a good thing. I've been thinking about Drake and something my father once said. You can never trust a salesman.''

''Oh, Mel, that's generalizing and not at all fair. You might as well say all models are dumb.''

"And we are! Otherwise we'd be doing something else. Nothing worse than being wanted for your outside packaging alone. What I would give for a guy who liked me for the person I am inside and not for what I look like!"

"It's easy to say that, Mel, when you look like you do. When you look like I used to, you never have a chance for a guy to like *any* part of you, the outside *or* the inside."

"You always say things like that. I don't believe you were ever that ugly."

"Maybe not ugly, but I was fat."

"Codswallop. You were probably just pleasantly plump. I'll have you know a lot of men like a bit of meat on a girl. Besides, you would still have been very pretty. You've got the sweetest face with the loveliest of eyes. They don't even need to be made-up to look good. I'd kill for eyes like that. I have to put a truckload of stuff on mine to look half as good as yours do first thing in the morning."

"Oh, go on with you. You're such a flatterer."

"No, I'm not. Trust me on this. I never flatter other girls, not even my best friend."

Zoe's heart squeezed tight. She'd never had a best friend before. It was so much better than being just a roommate.

"Yes, you would, Mel," Zoe returned warmly. "You pretend to be tough, but you're not at all. You're as soft as butter."

"Now who's the flatterer," Mel protested. But she sounded pleased.

"I'd better get going, or my phone bill will be bigger than Ben Hur."

"You be kind to yourself now."

"I will. I promise."

"And don't do anything I wouldn't do."

Zoe laughed. "That gives me a pretty broad canvas."

"It does indeed."

"See you tomorrow, Mel."

"'Bye, sweetie. Love you."

She ended the call, leaving Zoe with a warm fuzzy feeling in the pit of her stomach. There was nothing like hearing someone tell you that they loved you, especially when you felt they meant it.

Drake was always telling her that he loved her.

But did he mean it?

Zoe sighed, put her phone back in her handbag and headed for the door. What she needed was distraction from her carousel thoughts about Drake and those other equally perturbing thoughts about another man who never shaved and didn't wear nearly enough clothes!

The heat hit her the moment she stepped outside the door. The temperature had really shot up since her neighbor's early-morning visit. It was going to be scorching. She would have to find an air-conditioned shopping mall, that was for sure.

Unfortunately, Nelson Bay hadn't changed much since her last visit. Although it was the tourist hub of the Port Stephens area with a huge marina where you could take any number of cruises, the shopping center was still relatively small, with no mall to speak of.

After a couple of hours spent browsing in every air-conditioned store she could find, then lingering over brunch in a café down near the water, Zoe hesitated between actually going on a whale-watching cruise or trying out the local movie house, as she'd said to Mel. The movies won, again because of the air-conditioning, and also the choice available. A hard-edge action adventure flick which had an all-male cast. Consequently, no sex.

Zoe thought her poor brain—and body—deserved a rest from the subject.

The theater was small and crowded, with Zoe having to sit far too close to the screen with her head tipped back all the time. The movie wasn't too bad, but far too long, and by the time she emerged, she had serious cramps in her neck.

She was rubbing them and wandering back toward the spot where she'd parked her car when she passed a small store front advertising remedial massages.

The wooden door was closed, but there was an Open For Business sign hanging on it. Zoe had never had a massage before, but her boss was very partial to them.

What the heck, Zoe thought. It was still too early to go back.

Ten minutes later she was lying facedown on a massage table, dressed in nothing but her bra and panties, and feeling just a little bit self-conscious, despite the masseur being a woman. Her name was Glenda, a tall athletic woman in her mid-thirties who looked a bit like Zoe's sports coach at high school.

When she'd asked Zoe to strip down to her underwear, Zoe had been momentarily transported back to the gym dressing room where she'd been forced to change into a skimpy sports gear every Thursday afternoon.

Thinking back to those days, Zoe realized Mel was right. She'd only been pleasantly plump when she'd finally come to Sydney at the age of twenty, but back then, during her teenage years, she'd been fat. Fat as a pig. Her nickname in high school was Miss Piggy.

Yet she hadn't always been fat. In elementary school she'd been a slip of a thing. But when her mother died of cancer a few days after Zoe's thirteen birthday, Zoe had turned to food for comfort. That, along with the sudden onset of puberty, had turned her into a blob.

The teasing she'd endured over her weight had been pretty awful every single school day, but gym days had been unendurable. Maybe she'd been imagining it, but Zoe thought even the female sports coach had enjoyed some kind of perverse pleasure in seeing her struggle into the short pleated skirt and sleeveless top which showed off every appalling inch of her grossly overweight body.

It had taken Zoe years to eradicate the feelings of shame and self-loathing over her body. In truth, she probably still hadn't eradicated those old tapes entirely. Otherwise, she wouldn't be feeling self-conscious right now.

"You work out, don't you?" Glenda said as she bent Zoe's arms up into a comfortable position on top of the table, then unclipped her bra.

"Yes," Zoe admitted, a tad tautly. But she wasn't

used to this kind of thing. "A couple of times a week."

"You can always tell. You're looking good, girl."

"You really think so?"

"I'll say. Just don't overdo it. Nothing worse than women who work out too much. They begin to look sinewy. But you're just right. Now...let's see if we can do something about these knots in your shoulders and neck. Oh, yes...they're tight as a drum. I'll bet you're from Sydney. We get a lot of stressed out Sydney people up here. Just relax, love..."

Zoe did relax. To begin with. She settled her face into the hole in the table, closed her eyes and let all her muscles go, as per Glenda's instructions. But just as she was beginning to appreciate why Fran was addicted to such pampering, Zoe made the mistake of opening her eyes and looking down at the bright orange carpet.

Immediately, she thought of Aiden. Then last night's dream.

"Hey," Glenda said. "Don't tense up again. Relax."

Relax! How could she relax with last night's dream replaying in her brain?

Zoe squeezed her eyes tightly shut again and tried to banish the erotic fantasy from her mind, but it was impossible. Her lying there nearly naked didn't help. Neither did the fact she had to stay perfectly still. It wasn't the same as being bound to a bed, but it didn't take much imagination to once again summon up the deliciously seductive feelings of being a helpless captive. It was also very easy to pretend it wasn't Glenda's hands on her. But Aiden's.

He'd been so good with his hands in that dream. So very very good.

Zoe stifled a moan as Glenda started working up the back of her thighs toward her bottom.

"Do...do you think you could do my shoulders a bit more?" she said.

"Sure. Goodness, you're all tight there again. What on earth have you been doing to yourself lately?"

What, indeed?

"I guess I've been working too hard," Zoe said.

"Ever thought about changing your job?"

"Er...no. I actually quite like my job."

"Well, there's something in your life which you don't like, love. I suggest you find out what it is and change that!"

7

AFTER the massage, Zoe drove to a local restaurant for dinner, not wanting to cook. By the time she finally arrived back at Hideaway Beach it was getting on for nine and the sun had well and truly set. The air outside was not appreciably cooler, however, and the cottage was stifling from being closed up all day.

Zoe opened up the windows and put on the ceiling fans, but they didn't help all that much. She was still hot. No, she was *very* hot.

The idea of a cooling swim beckoned like a siren's voice and it seemed silly to deny herself the pleasure. Silly to keep hiding in this house as well. Aiden was not going to approach her again. Not at this hour. After her experiences during the massage, Zoe well understood why she'd made the decision to distance herself from his corrupting presence today, but enough was enough!

The decision made to have a swim, Zoe hurried to extract her swimsuit from her bag, pulling out the new black one-piece Mel had talked her into buying at the summer sales and which she hadn't dared wear in public yet. It had a low-cut square neckline which just covered her nipples and was perilously high cut at the sides. You really had to keep your bikini line waxed well to wear it, but that was no trouble to Zoe. She kept everything waxed well.

Five minutes later, she was plunging headfirst into the ocean, surfacing with a gasp. After the intense heat of the day the water was wonderfully refreshing. Unfortunately, she was standing right at the spot where the waves broke so she had to jump up and down all the time, which was rather tiring. A few feet farther out it was almost flat, with just a small swell. There, she could lie back and wallow in the more gentle waves, without getting exhausted or being knocked off her feet.

Zoe wasn't a great swimmer, but competent enough. She'd been taught properly at elementary school and back then, before she'd turned into a blob, she'd spent many a hot summer's day swimming in the local creek.

Diving under the breaking waves, she quickly reached her objective where she was able to float quite successfully. With her hands behind her head, she stared up at the star-studded night sky and tried to work out which ones formed the Southern Cross. She thought she'd found it several times.

Time drifted. And so did she. Zoe didn't realize 'til she decided to swim back in just how far out she was. It gave her a fright, as did the current her feet encountered when she tried to tread water. It was strong and pulling her, not toward the beach, but toward the bluff stretching out into the ocean, where rolling waves were crashing against the jagged black rocks.

Zoe struck out for the shore with slightly panicky strokes, but made little headway against the strength of the rip. When she stopped swimming, it dragged her sideward and backward. Toward the rocks.

Searching the ocean, Zoe couldn't see another single soul. Even the moonlit beach looked deserted. Everyone had gone home. Or gone out. There weren't any lights on in any of the weekenders, except Nigel's and Aiden's.

Would he hear her if she cried out? His house seemed so far away. She didn't want to die.

Damn it, she *wasn't* going to die!

Zoe started screaming for help and swimming at the same time, kicking like mad.

AIDEN was sitting up in an armchair by the window, trying to read, when he thought he heard a faint cry.

His head jerked up from the book, his ears instantly on alert. A gull? The wind perhaps?

The cry came again. Then again. And again.

Aiden was on his feet and running.

Not a bird. A woman. And she was in trouble.

He burst out of his front door, leaped down the three front steps and sprinted across the beach, scanning the ocean as he went. He spotted her about fifty feet out, right down the end where the rocks were.

It was Zoe. He just knew it was Zoe.

Aiden didn't stop to speculate on what she was doing out there at this time of night. He whirled and raced back to pick up his board which was thankfully leaning against the front porch. Adrenaline had him covering the sand back to the water's edge in no time. He ran through the shallows, threw the board across the first wave, dived facedown onto it and paddled like crazy.

If he'd been in one of those lifeguard rescue races, he'd have won hands down, so fast did he cover the distance from the water's edge to where Zoe was valiantly swimming and getting nowhere fast. Once drawn alongside her, he sat up, reached over to grip her under the arms then hauled her up across the board in front of him.

Their eyes connected for a second, hers still wide with fear, his appalled at what might have happened if he hadn't heard her cry out.

"What were you doing," he snapped, "swimming so far out at this time of night? You could have got a cramp and drowned, or been taken by a shark, or smashed against the rocks. You have a death wish or something?"

His own eyes widened with this last accusation. "Hey, that wasn't the idea, was it?" he threw at her. "You weren't trying to kill yourself, were you?"

Zoe didn't have the strength to defend herself verbally, but her face must have told him the truth.

"Sorry," he muttered. "I should have known you weren't the suicidal type. Not much of a rescuer, am I, bawling you out like that. I guess you were just hot and went for a swim, then got caught in the tide. I should have thought to warn you about the tide here this morning, but you made me so mad I just didn't think."

"Same here," she choked out.

Suddenly, she began to shiver violently.

Aiden swore, but Zoe knew it wasn't at her.

His hands were gentle as they shifted her 'round 'til she was lying lengthwise on the front of the board, her back leaning up against his chest. His *bare* chest, she noticed, despite everything.

Did he spend his whole life half naked?

Another shiver ran down her spine. A different sort of shiver.

"Don't worry," he said softly, rubbing her goose-bumped arms up and down. "You're in shock. You'll be right once I get you home and into a hot shower."

Zoe tried to protest when they reached the shore and Aiden swept her up off the board into his arms. But he silenced her with a look, and a sharp, "Don't you think you've been silly enough for one night?"

She closed her eyes and sagged against him.

"That's better," he said, satisfaction in his voice.

Zoe groaned silently, any physical exhaustion she'd been feeling swiftly overridden by the much more powerful feelings she'd been trying to fight all week-end.

Lust, hot and strong, flooded every pore of her flesh, heating her from the inside out, bringing with it an exquisitely tortuous awareness of Aiden's body. Her eyes being shut only intensified the experience. She wallowed in the strength of the arms carrying her; the warm wet wall of chest pressing against the side of her breast; his thighs slapping against her bottom as he strode across the sand.

He was taking her to his place, she knew. Into a hot shower, he'd said.

Oh, God…

The sensible part of Zoe's brain warned her not to

let him take her into the setting of one of her wildest fantasies about him. But she was too far gone for common sense, or willpower, or any high moral ground.

She felt weak with desire, driven by cravings so strong they amazed her. She wasn't used to wanting a man this much. She'd never wanted Drake like this. Lust, she decided despairingly, was nothing at all like love.

Lust focused on one thing and one thing only.

The physical.

She tensed when she felt him mounting some steps, keeping her eyes tightly shut whilst he opened his front door then carried her through, angling her body so that her feet didn't hit anything.

Zoe's heart began to pound.

It was warm inside, but not unbearably so.

He crossed a short distance, then lowered her down onto something soft and squishy. A couch by the feel of it. Leather.

She opened her eyes, then wished she hadn't. For he was looming over her in just the way she'd once imagined.

"Glad to see you're still alive," he said. "I was just about to do mouth-to-mouth resuscitation."

The thought of his mouth on hers banished what little was left of her scruples and she looked deep into his eyes, unable to hide her feelings for him any longer.

Not *wanting* to.

"I'd have liked that," she whispered, and a ripple of exquisite excitement ricocheted down her spine.

He was taken aback. No doubt about that.

But only for a second or two.

His eyes darkened with a desire of his own as he stared down at her mouth. He sat down on the edge of the couch and reached to lift some wet strands of hair away off her face. Her lips puffed apart with a soft gasp.

He didn't say a word, for which she was glad. Words would have shattered the dizzying sense of anticipation which was twisting her stomach into knots. His hands curled over her shoulders and his mouth started to descend. Zoe's heart thudded wildly.

But his head didn't come all the way down. His grip tightened on her shoulders and he drew her up toward him…slowly…then swiftly, their mouths colliding.

Zoe's valiantly suppressed passion for him was unleashed with a rush, her arms wrapping tightly 'round his torso, her mouth as hungry as his. He groaned then pushed her back down onto the couch where he kissed her 'til she thought she might die from lack of air.

He finally stopped, his breathing ragged as he sat back up abruptly, his gaze sweeping down over her own rapidly panting chest. "Let's get this off," he said, and swiftly peeled the almost-dry swimsuit from her fired-up flesh, tossing it carelessly aside.

A stunned Zoe watched it land across a black lacquered cabinet which held a big black stereo. With a single wide-eyed glance, she registered the rest of the room, which was almost as colorful as the outside of the house. Lemon walls. White woodwork. Terracotta ceiling.

The furniture was eclectic. A mixture of old and new. Glass-topped, wood-based and wrought-iron pieces sat side by side. The soft furnishings were just as varied, the colors bold. The drapes were black silk and the leather couch she was lying on was a deep burnt orange.

"That's better."

Aiden's speaking again brought her back to the reality of her lying stark naked in front of him, in quite bright light. Yet oddly, she wasn't besieged by concerns over her body shape or grooming, as she was when she was with Drake. It didn't seem to matter that she had no makeup on, or her hair was sticky with saltwater and hanging down in rattails. If the look in Aiden's eyes was anything to go by, he still liked what he saw.

And she liked what she saw. She couldn't wait for Aiden to strip off as well and for her to see if *all* her fantasies about his body were true.

She swallowed at the thought.

But he didn't undress. He pushed her left leg off the couch and sat down where it had been lying, leaning forward over her body, his hands skimming over the surface of her rapidly heating skin, grazing up over the tips of her breasts.

Zoe gasped, then groaned with disappointment when his hands moved on over her collarbones and up her throat to her face. Holding the sides of her head, he bent down 'til their mouths were almost touching, but not quite. His tongue darted out to lick at her parched lips, working its way right around them. It wasn't 'til he stopped that Zoe realized she'd been holding her breath, not knowing what to do, or what to expect.

Drake had never kissed her like this before, if you could call what Aiden had just done, kissing.

"Give me your tongue," he ordered thickly.

She hesitated a fraction before sliding it slowly out between her tingling lips. She quivered when he touched the tip with his own tongue tip, then shuddered when he sucked on it.

He let it go, his head lifting slightly, his eyes frowning down at her.

She blinked up at him, her own head spinning.

"What?" she said, finding it hard to think clearly.

"Don't you like that?"

"I...I'm not sure," she admitted. "But don't stop."

He laughed a low, deliciously sexy laugh. "No fear of that, honey. I've been wanting to make love to you since you smiled at me yesterday. I've thought of nothing else but you all day."

"I...I've been thinking of you, too," she confessed.

"That's gratifying to hear. I was beginning to think I'd lost my touch. But let's not talk. We can talk later. We can talk tomorrow." His head descended again and he kissed her for real, deep, drugging kisses which had the blood pounding in her temples and her body racing like a Formula One Ferrari on the starting blocks.

She moaned when his mouth abandoned her, then

moaned again when he rubbed his stubbly chin over her breasts. Her rock-hard nipples felt like they were on fire. He licked one, then sucked on it as he had in her dream.

An electric charge zigzagged down through her stomach, centering between her thighs. She cried out and her back arched away from the couch, her hands somehow finding his hair. He stopped momentarily to lift her hands up above her head, out of the way, and they flopped back over the wide leather arm of the couch. His lips returned to take possession of her other breast, his right hand squeezing it at the same time, pushing the whole areola and nipple deeper into his mouth. When Zoe's back went to arch again, Aiden's other hand splayed across her tautly held stomach, his large palm pressing her back down against the leather, keeping her spine still, keeping *her* still whilst he continued his erotic feasting on her breasts.

The effect was incredible, her mind as turned on as her body. She writhed against those captive hands, crying out with the heady mixture of pleasure, and yes, pain. For every now and then he would nip at a nipple with his teeth, then tug on it. Zoe would suck in sharply with relief once he released the pained peak, only to perversely want him to do it again almost straight away. She swiftly became addicted to the tortuously erotic experience, never wanting him to stop.

But he did stop, and the hand on her belly moved down into the damp curls which guarded the most intimate parts of her body. His mouth followed, lick-ing at her navel whilst those knowing fingers parted, probed and penetrated. She gasped, then gritted her teeth. He was touching her in even more ways than he had in her dream, knowing exactly where and how to give her the most exquisite yet almost mind-bending pleasure. She couldn't think. She could only feel, and crave more.

"Please," she begged, her head thrashing from side to side. "Oh, please..."

He responded by flipping her right leg over his shoulder and putting his mouth where his hand had been. When she jackknifed, he gripped her bottom, lifting it, and her hips, away from the leather, giving him better access and stopping any further movement from her.

Oh...!

Drake had *never* done this to her. Never. She hadn't wanted him to. The thought had repulsed her. Aiden had done it briefly to her in her dream and she hadn't been repulsed then, but that had been fantasy. This was real!

Yet there was no embarrassment, only the most intense pleasure. And the most urgent need.

Yes, yes, she craved. *There! There!*

His tongue flicked over her swollen clitoris and she almost screamed. Another flick. Then another. She clenched her teeth harder in her jaw. She was going to come. She was sure of it. He only had to touch it with his tongue again.

He didn't touch it with his tongue again. Instead, his lips closed over the burning bursting nub of flesh and he sucked on it. Hard.

She screamed, then splintered apart, coming as she had *never* come before. Her back arched. Her mouth gaped wide. Her head exploded with a thousand stars. Brilliant and blinding. The spasms went on and on and on, wave after wave, 'til at last, it was over.

Aiden's head lifted, his expression both smug and slightly sheepish.

"I'll have to leave you to go to the bathroom for a minute or two. Your...um...enthusiasm...tipped me over the edge as well. Which is not such a tragedy, under the circumstances. Next time, we can enjoy the real thing together, and for much longer than I was anticipating. Don't go away now," he added, giving her bottom an affectionate smack before lifting her leg off his shoulder and placing it gently back down on the couch.

Zoe lay there, dazed, her other leg still dangling over the side of the sofa. She didn't have the strength to drag it up into a more modest position. Her arms were still flopped over her head and she felt...wonderful. She knew she should get up, make some excuse and leave. But she didn't have the will-power, or the desire.

The *next* time, he'd said. Had he meant tomorrow, or later tonight, after he'd rested awhile? Zoe knew that a man needed some time before he could make love again.

She winced at using that expression, for what Aiden had just done to her had nothing to do with love. It was just sex to him, the same kind of *just sex* sex Drake had had with that blonde. Yet despite knowing that, Zoe had enjoyed it far more than any lovemaking of Drake's.

This realization brought a degree of bewilderment. She'd always believed love made sex better. Certainly sex with Drake had been better than sex with Greg. That experience had been gross!

But this...this was something else yet again...

The bathroom door opened and Aiden walked back into the room, scattering all Zoe's attempts to make sense of this situation.

He was naked. And still stunningly erect.

Zoe couldn't help staring at him. Her fantasies had underestimated things a tad. "I thought you'd said that you'd...um..." Her voice trailed off as he approached her.

"I did," he agreed smilingly. "Just shows you what happens when you haven't had sex for a long while. Time to adjourn to my boudoir, I think," he said, and bent to scoop her back up into his arms.

He carried her over to another door, holding her easily with one arm whilst he opened it and flicked on the overhead light. It lit up a roomy bedroom with polished floorboards, royal-blue walls and ceiling, colorful Indian rugs and a huge brass bed that was startlingly similar to the one in her dream.

She stared at the four solid brass posts stationed at each corner and tried not to picture herself spread-eagled on top of the prettily embroidered white bedspread which looked perversely virginal.

Zoe didn't think there'd been too many virgins gracing this bed, no matter what Aiden said about not having sex for a long time. He probably thought a week was a long time.

''Don't say a word about the bedspread,'' he advised on seeing the expression and direction of her eyes. ''My mother made it for me and I like it.'' With that, he threw back the spread with one hand, revealing blue sheets.

She blinked up at him. ''Your mother?''

''Everyone has one,'' he returned dryly, and lowered her into the middle of the mattress. ''But we're not going to chitchat about family tonight. Or boyfriends, or being free, or any other emotional baggage. We're going to just enjoy each other, right?''

''Right,'' she choked out, trying not to stare at the part of him she was hoping to enjoy most.

He pulled open the bedside drawer and extracted a box of condoms. Stripping off the cellophane wrapping, he flipped open the lid, and tipped it upside down, at least seven or eight small packets spilling out.

''Don't let me forget to use them,'' he told her as he climbed back onto the bed and drew her into his arms. ''You've got me into such a state, it's the sort of stupid thing I might do.''

He didn't forget. And neither did Zoe.

But she forgot everything else. Drake. Her conscience. Her common sense. And every inhibition she thought she had.

They were to return later, along with the shock and the shame of it all. She was no better than Drake. Worse, even.

Zoe was infinitely grateful that Aiden was asleep when she crept out of his house just before the dawn.

8

AIDEN woke with a start. And an immediate sense of something not being right.

He rolled over and realized what was wrong.

The other side of the bed was empty.

Zoe wasn't there.

''Zoe?'' he called out, hoping against hope she'd just gone to the bathroom. Or the kitchen, maybe. ''Zoe, are you there?''

No answer. There was no noise but the sound of gulls and waves slapping against the sand.

Throwing back the quilt, Aiden jumped out of bed and raced over to the window which gave him a view of Nigel's cottage and the road above it.

Her car was gone. Zoe was gone.

He swore.

She'd run away. Back to Sydney. Back to a lover who didn't love her. Back to a life which had obviously been making her miserable.

Aiden swore again.

She hadn't been miserable last night. She'd been in heaven.

He'd been in heaven, too. He'd never known a girl like Zoe before. She'd been so...he couldn't think of a word to describe her. Or to describe what making love with her was like. All he knew was he'd never experienced the like before.

One night simply hadn't been enough.

Yet it would have to be enough, wouldn't it?

Zoe had made the decision to leave what they'd shared at a one-night stand. To chase after her would be ridiculous.

Yet that was what Aiden was tempted to do.

"Don't be such a romantic fool," he muttered, and threw himself back into bed. "You've been given the perfect out from getting further involved, so be grateful for small mercies and forget her."

But forgetting Zoe wasn't all that easy, especially with the sheets still smelling of her female body. In the end, Aiden was forced to get up and try to rid the room of that tormentingly musky scent.

Stripping the bed clean, however, was no cure for what was ailing Aiden. Zoe was still there, in his mind. Finally, he resorted to pacing around the house, haranguing himself with cold hard logic.

"Get this straight, you dumb fool! You're nothing special to Zoe. Sleeping with you was just an impulse. She was feeling lonely and unloved and you were just there, ready, willing and able to give her a little of which she needed most at the time. Okay, a *lot* of what she needed most," he added testily. "That still doesn't mean a thing. Get real, man. Last night was just a one-night stand to her. Face it and forget it. Forget *her.*"

But even as he said those last words, his memory was propelling him back to the night before and all that had transpired between them.

He hadn't made love that many times in one night for donkey's years. He just couldn't seem to get enough of her. He'd never known a girl so responsive, yet at the same time so surprised by her responses. That was what got to him the most. The look in her eyes when he touched her. The sounds she made when he entered her.

They were addictive, those sounds. He wanted to hear them over and over. Those initial gasps of surprise. Then those soft moans of pleasure. But most of all the way she cried out when she came.

Aiden's male ego was fiercely flattered by the intensity—and frequency—of Zoe's orgasms.

Was he deluding himself in thinking she would not have found so much pleasure with any other man? And was he deluding himself in thinking *he* couldn't experience the like with any other woman?

Common sense insisted yes, he *was* deluding himself. To both questions. If Zoe had been seriously blown away by last night, she would have stayed. She would not have upped and scampered back to Sydney.

As for himself….

He'd had some great sex in his life, with a lot of different girls. Probably, the only reason his experience with Zoe stood out was because it came at the end of six months' celibacy. Naturally, he'd enjoyed it to the nth degree. What red-blooded man wouldn't?

He really had to put what had happened between them into context. They'd been ships passing in the night. For whatever reason, Zoe had needed a man and he'd obviously needed a woman. There'd been no special connection. No romantic overtones. It had been a strictly sexual encounter.

Aiden mulled over this last thought. If it had been a strictly sexual encounter on Zoe's side, then why had she run away? Wouldn't she have stayed the rest of the weekend in his bed for more of the same?

He was to think about that question for the rest of the day.

THE drive back to Sydney was a blur, but Zoe made it in good time, owing to the light traffic and excellent weather. It was just on ten as she let herself into her apartment.

Mel immediately emerged from her bedroom, dressed in her favorite blue silk shortie pajamas. "When you said you were getting on the road early this morning," she said, pushing her long blond hair out of her face, "I didn't think you meant *this* early. No, you don't have to worry. Ron's not here. I didn't let him stay the night and he was seriously displeased. But that's another story. Want some coffee?"

Zoe found a smile from somewhere. "That would be lovely."

"You look tired," Mel threw over her shoulder as they both made their way down to the kitchen. "No sleep, or difficult drive?"

"Bit of both." No way was she going to tell Mel about what had happened with Aiden.

Not that Mel would make a big deal out of it. No doubt she'd be very understanding, but she'd also want to know every single sordid detail. Zoe didn't want to relive what had to be the most shameful night of her life. The only positive aspect to come out of her disgusting behavior was that she finally and completely understood what Drake meant about a ''just sex'' encounter.

''So what have you decided to do about Drake?'' Mel asked as she made them both a mug of coffee.

''I'm going to forgive him. If he'll forgive *me,* that is,'' she added ruefully.

''For what?''

Several images came to mind, and it was a struggle not to blush. ''For going away without telling him where, of course,'' she answered. ''He still hasn't rung? Or called here personally?''

''Not a peep out of him.''

Zoe frowned. ''I wonder if he rang me at work on Friday afternoon. I'll call Fran later and find out. So what's all this about you not letting Ron stay the night?'' she asked, deftly changing the subject. ''That's not like you.''

Mel pulled a face. ''Oh, he started getting all jealous and possessive last night. You know how I can't stand that. Frankly, he irritated me all evening and in the end, I simply didn't want to sleep with him. He wasn't impressed, I can tell you.''

''Are you sure you weren't just finding fault because you want an excuse to break up with him?''

''Why on earth would I do that?''

''Because of that other fellow,'' Zoe said dryly. ''The rich one you don't feel attracted to.''

Mel blinked, then laughed. ''You know, you might be right. I've been thinking about that arrogant so-

and-so quite a bit this weekend. I simply hadn't made the connection with my feelings toward Ron.''

''Be honest, Mel. You told me yourself that once you start noticing a new man, the old one is history.''

''Yeah, you're right. Hard to make love with one guy when your mind's on another.''

Zoe's mind flew immediately to Aiden. How long, she agonized, would she continue to think of him? How long before the memories of that incredible night faded to nothingness?

Never, she had to accept. Sex like that was impossible to completely forget.

But it was still only sex. And casual sex at that. The sort of sex Aiden indulged in whenever he felt the need.

Zoe was no man's fool. Not anymore. She knew exactly what kind of man Aiden was. A beach bum. A surfer. He didn't aspire. He had no ambition other than what wave he would catch that day. He made no solid plans for the future, leading a free-and-easy life with no responsibility and no commitment. Clearly, he had no regular girlfriend, either. He probably just picked up a girl whenever he felt horny. It might have been a while since he'd had sex, but he'd been well prepared, hadn't he? All those condoms at the ready!

Which was why, when she woke this morning in his arms and was tempted to stay, Zoe forced herself to get up and get out of there. She doubted he'd be too angry when he finally woke and found her gone. After all, he'd been well satisfied the night before. Frankly, she hadn't known a man could make love that many times in one night, or that he could find so many positions without leaving the bed. She'd especially liked it when he turned her sideward and…

''Excuse me,'' Mel said. ''Snap. Snap. Here's your coffee, dreamy Daniels.'' And she plonked a steaming mug on the kitchen counter in front of where Zoe was standing.

''Thanks,'' Zoe managed to say without looking as hot and bothered as she was suddenly feeling. Damn Aiden. Why did he have to be such a fantastic lover? It was just as well he was living up at Hideaway Beach, well out of reach. Goodness knew what she would do if he'd been a Sydneysider.

She lifted the mug and started to sip.

The front doorbell ringing had Zoe's head jerking up from the drink. ''Are you expecting anyone?'' she asked Mel.

''No. And I'm not dressed, so I can't answer it. If it's Ron, tell him I went home for the day. He's dumb enough to believe anything.'' And she scuttled off to her room, taking her coffee with her.

Zoe's heart raced as she approached the door. Logic insisted it couldn't be Aiden. For one thing he had no idea where she lived. He didn't even know her second name.

Yet perversely, she wanted it to be him.

She held her breath as she swept open the door.

It wasn't Aiden. It was Drake.

She stared at him for a long moment, thinking he wasn't a patch on Aiden in the looks department, even with his smart clothes and perfect grooming.

When Drake stared right back at her, Zoe suddenly

remembered she had no makeup on and her hair was a mess. She had showered after leaving Aiden's bed, and thrown on some shorts and a T-shirt, but that had been the extent of her efforts.

"So I was right," he snapped, stalking past her into the apartment. "You didn't go off to some secret destination for the weekend at all." He spun 'round to face her. "That wretched Fran insisted you had when I dropped by your office late on Friday, and I actually believed her. But I got to thinking over the weekend and I finally realized it wasn't at all like my Zoe to do something like that."

Any intention Zoe had of being apologetic and forgiving was temporarily sidelined by his pompous and almost patronizing attitude. She swung the door shut and crossed her arms, struggling to keep her irritation under control.

"I *did* go away," she informed him curtly, biting her tongue lest she add she'd done a lot more than go away for the weekend. She'd gotten herself well and truly laid, and by a far better lover than him!

Guilt consumed her the moment this last thought entered her head. For in all honesty, Drake was quite a good lover. It was just that she was different with Aiden than she was with him. More relaxed. And consequently, far more orgasmic. And how!

"I just got back," she said, not wanting to think about that.

He looked her up and down again. "You look a bit travel worn. Back from where, might I ask? Or am I not to be told where you went as part of my punishment?"

Zoe sighed and uncrossed her arms. ''I wasn't trying to punish you, Drake. Not really. I just needed time to think.''

''Then tell me where you went.''

''Does it matter?''

''It does, if you want us to get back together again.''

Zoe stiffened. ''I don't like ultimatums.''

''And I don't like being given the runaround. Either you love me or you don't. Either you forgive me or you don't. Either you want us to have a relationship or you don't. I've apologized for what happened down in Melbourne. And I've promised you faithfully not to do it again. I can do no more. Now the rest is up to you. So I'm asking you again, where did you go this weekend?''

For a split second, Zoe was tempted to tell him to go away. But then she remembered how lonely life would be without him. It wasn't as though she had any future with the likes of Aiden. No doubt he was at this very moment very relieved that she'd done a flit and left last night at a one-night stand. Men like him ran a mile from commitment, or complications.

''At a little beach near Port Stephens,'' she confessed. ''I...I stayed at a motel.'' Zoe thought it best not to mention she'd stayed at Nigel's weekender. Drake didn't like Nigel one little bit. He was scathing about all men—and women—who weren't straight.

''I see.'' His head cocked on one side and he smiled one of his most charming smiles. ''You know...I rather like your hair like that. I didn't realize it was naturally curly.'' He reached out and picked up a curl, winding it 'round his finger, then looping it behind her ear. "You should wear it like this more often on the weekends. It looks sexy. *You* look sexy. You're not wearing a bra, either, are you?" he said, his right hand sliding up underneath her T-shirt toward her left breast. She gasped when he touched a nipple which was still hard and aching from the night before.

"God, I've missed you, Zoe," he groaned, sliding his other arm around her waist and bending his head to nuzzle at her neck. "There's no one like you. I love it that you haven't slept around, that you're so sweet and nice." His mouth traveled up her throat, and all the while his hand was cupped around her breast, his thumb pad rolling over the sensitized peak.

A moan escaped her mouth. But the feeling was more discomfort than pleasure. Soon she was screaming inside her head. When his lips finally covered hers and his tongue started to push into her mouth, she gagged and wrenched herself away.

"No!" she cried out.

"What?" For a moment he looked stunned, then merely angry. "More punishment, Zoe? Is that what this is?"

"No," she said shakily, shocked by her reaction to Drake's lovemaking. "I...I just don't want to. It's too soon. I...I need a bit more time. I can't stop thinking about you and that blonde." Which might have been the case last Friday, but no longer. What Zoe couldn't stop thinking about this morning was herself and Aiden.

‘‘When do you think it will not be too soon, then?’’ he bit out.

‘‘I don’t know.’’

‘‘Don’t cut off your nose to spite your face, Zoe. You were enjoying what I was doing just then. Your nipple was like a rock.’’

She didn’t have the heart to tell him the truth. That it wasn’t him who’d aroused her.

‘‘I love you, Zoe. And I need you. Don’t make me wait too long.’’

‘‘Is that a threat?’’

‘‘No. A fact. When a man loves a woman as I love you, he wants to make love to her.’’

Zoe stared at him. He was right, and vice versa. Why, then, didn’t *she* want to make love with *him* anymore? If she loved him, she would.

Maybe it *was* just too soon. Maybe a bad conscience was the culprit here, that’s all. Maybe in time, everything would be all right.

Drake looked belligerent before suddenly backing down, his eyes softer. ‘‘Look, I do realize I hurt you. A lot. And yes, I can understand you might need some time to completely forgive and forget. How about I leave you in peace this week and give you some space to get over things?’’

‘‘I’d appreciate that,’’ she said.

‘‘But come next Saturday night, I’m having one of my parties, and I’d really like you to co-host it, as you have for the last few times. I don’t want to have to explain my girlfriend’s absence to my clients and colleagues. Would you do that for me?’’

Zoe could not think of a reason to refuse. "Of course I will."

"You're a doll. And you'll help get the food and everything ready that day? As you know, I do have to work on Saturdays. It's our busiest day of the week."

"If you want me to."

"If I want you to! I'd be lost without you. You're such a wonderful organizer. And hopefully, by then, you'll feel comfortable about staying the night."

"Maybe..."

"I promise I won't press if it's still too soon."

Zoe suddenly realized Drake was bending over backward to be understanding and accommodating. Guilt consumed her anew.

"I'm sorry for being so difficult."

"That's perfectly all right, darling. I understand. Honest. The fault was all mine."

Zoe wished he wouldn't say things like that. It made her feel rotten. She would just die if Drake ever found out what she'd done.

Thankfully, there was little chance of that. She had no intention of confessing, and the chance of running into Aiden down here in Sydney was minimal. Even if by some incredible coincidence they did, Zoe doubted Aiden would make an embarrassing scene the way that blonde had done. That wouldn't be his style.

Drake pulled out his wallet and counted out five hundred-dollar bills. "Here," he said. "Buy yourself a smashing new dress for the party."

"Oh, no, no, I couldn't," she protested, shaking her head and refusing to take them.

"But why ever not?" He seemed genuinely perplexed. And he had every right to be. It wasn't the first time he'd bought her clothes and she'd never objected before.

"Well, I…I…"

"Don't be silly," he said, and pressed the money into her hands. "Just make sure it's not too revealing. Can't have all those playboys I sell penthouses to lusting after your perfect little body and trying to chat you up. Not that you'd look twice at any other man. That's the thing I value most about you, darling. Your lovely old-fashioned standards. I could trust you with any man in any situation. But I'll get going now and leave you to have a rest. You do look a little tired. I'll be in touch before Saturday by phone. That okay?"

"I guess so," she said weakly.

"Great. Look after yourself and don't work too hard this week." He bent to peck her softly on the cheek. Then left.

Tears filled Zoe's eyes by the time she shut the door behind him.

I could trust you with any man in any situation.

Oh, Drake. If only you knew.

9

AIDEN dialed the only telephone number committed to his memory and waited for his mother to answer. It rang several times before she picked up.

"Kristy Mitchell," came her softly lyrical voice, sounding just a little fuzzy around the edges, as though she'd just got out of bed.

Given it was only eight-fifteen in the evening, Aiden didn't think she'd been asleep. He smiled. Same old Mom. He wondered who her latest lover was and if he knew he had no chance of either moving in with her or marrying her. His mom was not a marrying kind of woman.

Much like he was not a marrying kind of man. Perhaps it was in the genes.

"Hi, there, honey-bunch," he said in greeting. "How's my best girl?"

"Aiden!" she cried. "Oh, how lovely to hear your voice. I was just thinking about you."

"In what way?"

"If you really want to know, I was wondering when you were going to give up all that celibacy nonsense and get back to normal again."

"Well, actually, Mom, I, er..." His voice trailed off rather suggestively.

''You didn't! I don't believe it. At last! Who was she?''

''Just a girl.''

''Just a girl my foot! She'd have to be something special to drag you out of your self-imposed monkhood. The last time I talked to you, you were adamant that you still wanted nothing to do with the opposite sex. You said life was much happier without females in it.''

''Yeah and I was right,'' he snapped, giving in to the spleen which had been building all day.

''Oh, dear. You sound upset. What happened, sweetie?''

''I don't want to talk about it,'' he grumped.

''Of course you do. That's why you called me. Just wait a second 'til I get myself a glass of wine.''

Aiden was left dangling for a minute or two whilst his mother collected one of her favorite creature comforts.

He smiled wryly at how little time it had taken for her to find out the reason behind his call. She was a very astute woman, especially when it came to her one and only son. Because of course he *had* rung her to talk about Zoe. He just didn't like to admit it. He was twenty-eight years old. He should know his own mind by now. And know what he wanted out of life. It galled him that he still felt at sea on such matters.

''I'm back,'' she trilled. ''Now don't go being a typical male. I want the whole unvarnished truth, not some edited version to flatter your ego.''

Aiden sighed. Maybe this wasn't such a good idea after all. But it was too late now. So he told her the whole unvarnished truth, right down to the bit where Zoe did a bunk whilst he was still asleep.

"Mmm," was her initial highly instructive comment.

"Is that all you've got to say?"

"Give me a moment, sweetie. I'm thinking, and trying to remember how I might have felt and acted when I was Zoe's age. How old did you say she was?"

"I have no idea. When I first met her last Friday I thought she was in her late twenties, but the next morning, without all that makeup on, she looked about eighteen. My guess is early to mid-twenties."

"And she's from Sydney. And she has a boyfriend. Not a married one, I hope."

"Zoe wouldn't have anything to do with a married man."

"You sound quite sure of that."

"I am."

"Mmm."

There was a wealth of underlying meaning in that "Mmm." Aiden wished he knew what it was.

"Whatever the case," his mother continued, "she still has a lover who's creating problems for her. Perhaps the man in question is her boss. What does she do for a living?"

"I have no idea about that either. But judging by the way she looked and dressed on Friday, she's no factory worker. Something in an office is my guess."

"And what does she think *you* do?"

"Er...not much."

"She didn't recognize you?"

''No.''

''And you didn't enlighten her,'' came the dry comment.

''No.''

''Oh, Aiden, Aiden. I thought I taught you to be straight with people, especially women.''

''I used to be. But where did it get me, Mom? In court, and in all the newspapers.''

''Nothing is to be gained by lying,'' she pronounced firmly.

''That's not true,'' he countered sharply. ''Marcie gained a million-dollar apartment full, a snazzy little sports car and two hundred thousand in cash.''

''Material assets count for nothing if you lose your soul, son.''

Aiden rolled his eyes. She was always talking like that. About souls and stuff. Yet she wasn't religious in the conventional sense of the word. There was nothing at all conventional about Kristy Mitchell.

''Yeah, well, maybe I've already lost mine.'' There was a time not so long ago when all he thought about was material assets.

''Don't be ridiculous. You have a wonderful soul. I know. I gave it to you.''

Nothing modest about his mother, either.

''But back to Zoe,'' she said. ''Are you thinking she might be your one true love?''

Aiden rolled his eyes again. Not the one-true-love thing!

''Now who's being ridiculous, Mom. I hardly know the girl.''

''I only knew your father one short week and he

was my one true love. I fell for him the moment I set eyes on him and there's never been another to touch him since. I couldn't even bear to be with another man for years afterward.''

Aiden smothered a groan. How often had he heard this same story, about the drop-dead gorgeous hunk she'd met at a party when she'd been sixteen. How she'd been immediately smitten. How he'd gotten her pregnant the same night and been tragically killed in a head-on smash with a truck a week later. He'd been riding a motorcycle at the time. And speeding, of course.

What a hero!

What an idiot.

''Yeah right, Mom. But I rather doubt dear old Dad felt the same way about you. It was more likely just sex. You yourself explained to me when I was a teenager that sex and love were two entirely different things, and not to confuse them.''

''So why are you?''

''Why am I what?''

''Confused. If you're so sure it was just sex, then let it go. Let *her* go.''

''I can't,'' he confessed.

''I see.''

''If you really do see, then tell me what to do.''

''You already know what you should do, Aiden. You just want me to give you a push in the right direction.''

''Meaning?''

''Meaning you should go after her and make sure

of both your feelings, one way or the other. Otherwise you'll always wonder.''

''I told you, Mom. I'm pretty sure it was just sex. Admittedly, it was the best sex I've ever had, but I reckon that was because I hadn't had any in such a long time. What do you think? That could be the reason, couldn't it?''

''It's possible, but you can't really speak for the girl though, can you?''

''I guess not,'' he agreed.

''Look, the least you can do is call your lawyer friend and make a few discreet inquiries about this girl. Find out a bit about her background and this boyfriend of hers.''

''Yes, I supposed there's no harm in that.''

''No harm at all. Keep me posted.''

''I'll do that.'' Having made up his mind, at least about his immediate course of action, Aiden felt infinitely better. ''Thanks, Mom. You're the best.''

''And don't you forget it!''

Aiden hung up, opened the drawer which contained his red leather address book and looked up Nigel's home phone number, dialing straight away before he changed his mind.

Nigel answered almost before it rang at the other end. ''How dare you call me again!'' he raged down the line. ''I told you not to. There's nothing more to be said. I won't forgive you, Jeremy, not even if you got down on your knees and begged. Not even if you…''

''It's not Jeremy,'' Aiden broke in before Nigel

could elaborate on what Jeremy might do on his knees to be forgiven. ''It's Aiden. Aiden Mitchell.''

''Oh. Aiden. Oh. Er. Right.'' Nigel cleared his throat. ''Sorry. Had a bit of a tiff with Jeremy and he keeps ringing.''

''So I gathered. Blotted his copybook, did Jeremy?''

''Unfaithful little... Can't keep it zipped up. But he *is* gorgeous,'' Nigel added, sighing wistfully. ''I guess I'll forgive him in the end. So what's up?''

''I need your help with something...''

It took Nigel 'til mid Monday morning to get the last of the information Aiden wanted and call him back.

''You're out of luck,'' he said. ''She's gone back to Drake. Which is a pity. I can't stand that sleaze-bag.''

Aiden felt like he'd been punched in the stomach.

So she'd forgiven her cheating boyfriend. Straight away. Raced right back into his arms the night after she'd spent with *him.*

When Nigel revealed last night the circumstances leading up to his lending Zoe his place, Aiden had been confident she wouldn't go back to someone who'd cheated on her. He'd also started thinking she might have fled his bed because she'd been confused and embarrassed. He'd started hoping that maybe she'd be interested in their getting back together again.

Just to see, of course, if there *was* any special connection between them.

''How do you know, Nigel?'' he asked, frowning.

"Did she actually say so? You didn't ask her any of this straight out, did you? I warned you not to mention me at all."

"Would I do that?" He sounded offended and incredulous at the same time. "*Moi?* The soul of tact and discretion? Lawyer to the stars? Never in a million years! Besides, Zoe and I are not on such friendly terms that I could ask her anything of a personal or intimate nature. Anything I know about this, I've found out through Fran, plus a sneaky peek at the card attached to the two dozen red roses sitting on Zoe's desk this morning. It read, 'To the sweetest, most understanding girl in the world. All my love, Drake.'"

Aiden's stomach tightened. Not much doubt about the situation now.

So what had *he* been? came the angry question. Revenge? Payback time?

Maybe *that* was what was behind Zoe's surprise at enjoying herself with him so much. She hadn't expected to. She'd been out for vengeance, not pleasure.

But she *had* found pleasure. A great deal of pleasure. Strange…if she loved this Drake so much.

Another explanation occurred to Aiden. Maybe she *didn't* love the boyfriend. Maybe she'd been lying about that. Maybe she was just with him for the money. Which explained why she'd enjoyed herself so much the other night, but why she'd still gone back to the boyfriend.

Aiden was rocked by this possibility. No way would he get mixed up with another female who wanted nothing from a man but his money.

But no sooner had he thought this than he remembered Zoe had already proven she wanted something from *him* other than his money. She'd wanted his body, over and over. Whatever had been her initial reason for letting him make love to her, true desire had soon taken over. Aiden knew when a girl was enjoying herself in his bed, and Zoe certainly had.

"How wealthy is this Drake?" he asked Nigel, trying to get the full picture here.

"Can't say precisely. I gather he's one hotshot of a real-estate salesman. He's sold oodles of those flash inner-city apartments with harbor views. Fran even bought one, which should tell you something. She's not an easy sell. He lives pretty high. Owns one of the apartments in the same building as Fran's. But I seriously doubt his bank balance would rival yours."

"Mmm."

"I always worry when you start mmming like that."

Aiden laughed. It seemed enigmatic mmming ran in the family. "Did you find out for me what branch our hot-shot salesman works at?"

"North Sydney."

"And the phone number?"

"What exactly are you going to do, Aiden?"

"That depends."

"On what?"

"On how I feel by the end of this week."

10

ZOE walked from room to room, checking that everything was ready for the party. The flowers. The music. The snacks. The drinks.

A superb buffet supper awaited in the kitchen. Nothing hot, just salads and seafood, plus a selection of mouthwatering desserts, all delivered straight from the best city store food hall.

Drake didn't expect her to cook on these occasions, just order what she thought necessary on his credit card, then be there to collect the food and set everything out. But even doing that was a lot of work for upward of fifty guests.

Drake wasn't keen on hiring waiters to walk around with trays at his parties. He preferred having everything laid out on tables placed strategically around the large living areas, as well as out on the terrace. He liked to create a relaxed, informal atmosphere where people had something to do besides stand stiffly around in groups. Drake found there was more mingling if the guests had to get their own food and drinks.

And he was right. His parties were always a huge success. Drake had his successful-host routine honed down. After answering the door personally for the first hour or so, he then continuously circulated, chatting and telling jokes and making people feel special. Zoe was left to welcome any stragglers after that, as well as ensure the snack bowls were kept filled, ice buckets replenished and supper served right on eleven.

Frankly, for all Drake's talk about wanting her by his side at this do, Zoe would not see all that much of him tonight.

She was glancing around, satisfying herself that everything was ready, when she noticed that the arrangement of fresh Australian flowers on the hall stand in the foyer looked a bit lopsided. She hurried over, changed the position of two of the waratahs, then stood back to inspect the result.

"Stop fussing, darling."

Zoe glanced over her shoulder to see that Drake had finally emerged from his bedroom, ready for the night ahead. He'd chosen to wear all black, a perfect foil for his apartment's largely gray-and-white decor. He looked sleek and successful, and yes, sexy, she supposed. Eight days ago, she certainly would have thought so.

So why didn't she now?

Normally, she would have complimented him on the way he looked, but she found the words would not come. She went back to fiddling with the flowers, even though she knew they were fine.

"Don't change another single solitary stem," he advised. "They're perfect. Everything's perfect. Now go and make *yourself* perfect before people start arriving. As much as I quite like you in those shorts, I can't wait to see you in that fantastic little number you bought. I'm so glad you splurged on a designer dress and not something off the peg. It wouldn't do for my image, you know, if some other female turned up tonight wearing the same dress as my girlfriend.''

''Yes, that *would* be a catastrophe, wouldn't it?'' she snapped before she could stop herself. But her nerves were suddenly stretched to breaking point.

This last week had been the longest and most agitating week of her life. Drake giving her time and space hadn't really worked at all. By Friday, her head was even more full of memories of her time up at Hideaway Beach, and her body strung tight with a frustration she'd never known before.

In an effort to find distraction from her never-ending fantasies about Aiden, she'd worked like a demon at the office, staying back late every night, clearing her In tray to perfection, catching up on filing and correspondence, and being so super efficient that even Fran hadn't been able to find fault. Not once. Which was a first. Fran was a very demanding boss.

Then last night after work she'd spent hours looking for the sort of party dress Drake would approve of. Not that she was complaining. The lengthy shopping expedition had kept her busy, and her mind blissfully Aiden-free for a while.

She'd finally settled on a mauve satin slip dress which wasn't too revealing, courtesy of the bodice being overlaid with pink lace.

Unfortunately—or perhaps fortunately at the time—she had no shoes to match, and it had taken a further hour to find strappy pink-and-mauve imitation crocodile skin shoes.

She'd ended up spending more than the five hundred dollars Drake had given her, adding some of her own money. An unusual extravagance for Zoe. But she'd needed a lift, and she'd wanted to really please Drake.

Guilt, she supposed.

Lots of her actions this past week had been inspired by guilt.

This morning, she'd dragged her dream-haunted sleep-deprived body out of bed and driven over to Drake's place extra early where she'd propelled herself into all the preparations for the party with enthusiasm, angrily resolving not to think of Aiden anymore.

And it had worked to a degree. She'd even convinced herself that if she got nicely drunk tonight, she might be able to successfully go to bed with Drake after the party and rid herself of some of this hideous frustration.

But the moment Drake had come home from the office around five, cock-a-hoop about some wealthy world champion sportsman he'd snared as a client this afternoon, Zoe had found him infinitely irritating, especially when he told her he'd asked the wretched man to the party tonight.

As if he hadn't asked enough people already!

She'd been glad to have Drake disappear for the past hour into his room to shower and shave and dress, but the moment he'd reappeared, he'd rubbed her up the wrong way again, hence her sarcastic remark.

Drake glared at her across the room, his black eyes cold and angry.

Zoe shook her head at herself. She was acting exactly as Mel had done with Ron, deliberately finding fault and picking a fight. The difference in Mel's case, however, was that she'd got together with her new man this week, whereas *she* would never see Aiden again.

''I'm sorry,'' she said with a weary sigh. ''That was uncalled for. I'm just tired, and a little nervous. You know I hate making small talk with strangers, especially rich and famous strangers. I know very little about sport. What was it you said this new client of yours was world champion in?''

''*Ex* world champion, actually. And it's surfing.''

''Surfing!'' she echoed disbelievingly. Of all the sports in the world, Drake's client had to be involved in the one sport she didn't want to *think* about, let alone talk about.

Drake's expression was wry. ''I know. You never think of surfers as ever being seriously rich. But believe me, Mitch is.''

''Mitch,'' she repeated. ''Sounds American.''

''No, he's Australian through and through. Owns the Aus-Surf chain of stores. He started up several years ago with one small shop after injury forced him to retire early. Now Aus-Surf shops are franchised all around Australia. You must have seen them. They're everywhere.''

''Yes, yes, I have.'' They sold surfing equipment

and clothes and accessories. As much as she liked the beach, Aus-Surf gear was not quite Zoe's cup of tea. Too bright and bold.

"They're doing extra well at the moment," Drake rattled on, right in his element. Whenever he landed a wealthy client, he made it his business to find out all about him. "In the beginning, a lot of people thought the clothes were too loud and bright, but the surfing crowd loved them. Now that big colors have become all the rage in fashion, their sales have soared. Not that *I'd* ever be seen dead in that sort of thing. You should have seen what our multi-millionaire was wearing today. Can you imagine me in a lime-green shirt?"

"No," she said truthfully. But she could imagine Aiden. He'd look gorgeous in it. He'd look gorgeous in anything. He looked extra gorgeous in nothing.

Zoe sighed. Would it never stop, these thoughts?

"I know, I know," Drake said sheepishly. "I do rave on. Sorry. Go and get yourself ready. I'll get the ice ready for the drinks."

Zoe trailed off into the guest room where she'd put her things earlier, depression overwhelming her. All she wanted to do was run away, away from Drake, away from this party, and right away from playboy sportsmen who had egos larger than Mount Olympus and always thought they were God's gift to women. If she was strictly honest with herself, she wanted to run right back to Hideaway Beach. And to Aiden. She didn't care if he only wanted sex from her. That was all she seemed to want from him. It was certainly all she could think about.

Sometimes, she regretted running away from his bed last Sunday. She should have stayed, at least for the rest of the weekend. There was so much she hadn't done with him and which she'd since ached to do. Make love to him in a shower. In the ocean. With her on top. With her hands. Her mouth. Her breasts. One persistent fantasy was to tie *him* to that brass bed. To have him at her mercy. To drive him wild!

"Zoe!" Drake called out. "I don't hear that shower running. Get a move on, darling. Time's a wasting."

Zoe squeezed her eyes tightly shut. Oh, dear, what was she doing, wallowing in such thoughts? They were foolish. Futile. And so frustrating!

Yet, oh, the excitement they evoked. And the heat. She could feel it even now, spreading across her skin. A melting burning heat which scorched her face even as it seared between her thighs. She knew, without checking, that she would be wet. She'd been wet down there all week.

Groaning, she stripped off and plunged into a cold shower.

"Wow!" Drake exclaimed, when she emerged from the guest room fifty minutes later, looking cool and pretty in her mauve-and-pink dress. On the surface there was not a hint of the turmoil which was still rampaging beneath her seemingly controlled exterior.

She forced a smile as Drake walked slowly toward her, his dark eyes eating her up.

"I meet with your approval, do I?" she said.

"And how." He slid his arms around her waist and drew her close. "I might have to keep you really close by my side tonight. Can't have you swanning around by yourself looking this delicious, especially not with men like Mitch on the prowl.''

''I don't think you have to worry about me with men like this Mitch,'' she murmured ruefully, at the same time trying not to physically shrink away at the feel of Drake's hands on her. She managed not to look repulsed, but any hope she'd been harboring that she could go to bed with Drake tonight was well and truly dashed. There was just so much faking a girl could do in one lifetime.

''He's considered very handsome,'' Drake said. ''He's also looking for a penthouse to replace the one he had to hand over to his last girlfriend. She took him to court for breach of promise last year when he tried to dump her, and she won.''

''Good for her,'' Zoe said. ''Should be more of it.''

''Oh, I don't know. Men like that are a target for gold diggers. The girl in question said she gave up her career to live with him and look after him like a wife. She said he'd promised marriage but when she tried to set a date for their wedding, he told her he'd changed his mind, then tossed her out. His defense was that she was lying and that she'd only been house-sitting while he was traveling. But under oath he did admit to sleeping with her, though he claimed it was only once. If you saw the female in question, you'd know that stretched credibility. She was a stunner. Surely you must remember the case. It was in all the Sydney papers.''

''No. You know I don't read newspapers much.

And I rarely watch the news. It's always so miserable.''

''True. Still, it was your firm which handled the defense. Or should I say, the lovely Nigel. No wonder they lost.''

''I don't have much to do with Nigel and his clients,'' Zoe said stiffly, hating the way Drake spoke about gay men. ''Still, I think that had to be before I joined the firm. I've only been there five months, remember?''

''You're right. I think it was before that. But enough chitchat. God, you look good enough to eat,'' he growled, his head dipping to her neck.

''Drake, please,'' she said, wriggling out of his arms. ''It took me ages to get my makeup and hair just right.''

He stepped back and gave her a narrow-eyed look. ''You aren't going to knock me back again tonight, are you?''

Panic struck. ''You...you said you wouldn't press.''

''Did I?'' he said coldly. ''Silly me. Very well, Zoe, I won't press. But I wouldn't play this particular hand for too long, if I were you. I am not a patient man by nature.''

''I didn't say I *wouldn't* sleep with you tonight,'' she said, feeling wretched.

''How generous of you.''

''Drake, please, don't be like that. If you truly loved me, you'd understand.''

''If you truly loved *me,* this wouldn't be an issue.

You'd be only too happy to make up with me in bed.''

''It's not as simple as that for women.''

''It is for some,'' he muttered.

The doorbell ringing was a relief.

''We'll talk about this later,'' Drake said, firmly taking Zoe's arm and propelling her across the marble-floored foyer. ''Meanwhile, stop looking so grim and try smiling.''

''Bob!'' he exclaimed expansively on yanking open the front door. ''And Tracy! Now this is a surprise. But a pleasant one, I assure you.''

Zoe smiled at Bob whom she'd met before. He worked as a salesman for the same real-estate agency as Drake. About forty, balding, overweight, and divorced, Bob never missed one of Drake's parties.

She had no idea who Tracy was, but she was very attractive in a brassy bottle-blonde fashion. Thirtyish, she was wearing a short tight animal-print leather skirt and a black lace halter top with a deep crossover V neckline. Her hair was done up in that tousled just-got-out-of-bed look and her earlobes sported diamanté drop earrings which dangled down to her shoulders. Her breasts, which were big, were also braless, with large pointy nipples which were difficult to ignore under black lace.

''I don't think I've had the pleasure,'' Zoe directed at the blonde.

''Tracy is our new receptionist,'' Drake informed her a bit brusquely. ''My girlfriend, Zoe.''

Zoe smiled at Tracy who smiled sweetly back

whilst giving Zoe the once-over with her heavily made-up eyes.

''Bob, you sly dog, you,'' Drake went on with a suggestive chuckle. ''I had no idea you and Tracy were dating.''

''We're not, are we, love? Tracy kindly offered to come with me tonight when I complained I had no one to bring.''

''It was my pleasure, Bob, darling,'' the blonde returned brightly. ''And who knows? Maybe we'll do it again sometime. Well, well, so this is how you live, is it, Drake?'' She swept past them into the elegant columned foyer, showing everyone a rear view as provocative as her front. The top had no back to speak of, and she had an enviable behind, the shape of which Zoe knew would never be hers. A small tight butt, with narrow hips. Her legs were of enviable quality too, shapely calves and slender ankles, shown to advantage in black four-inch stilettos, complete with sexy ankle straps.

She made Zoe feel just a little girlish in her outfit. She suddenly wished she'd bought something sexier to wear.

The arrival of more guests was a welcome distraction and she was soon concentrating on her hostess role, all silly female jealousies banished from her mind. Drake handed over the doorman duties to her a good deal earlier than usual, which kept her busy. She tried not to worry about the fact he hadn't smiled at her, or spoken to her personally since their earlier altercation. She understood he was angry with her.

She also understood that if she didn't come across tonight, their relationship was over.

It was a dilemma Zoe didn't want to face 'til she had to. Meanwhile, she downed a couple of glasses of Chardonnay and waited for the alcohol to work. With a bit of luck, it might do the trick and she would suddenly find Drake attractive again. At worst, it would at least make her feel less tense and more relaxed.

The party was humming by ten, with Drake's prized new client not yet making an appearance. Clearly he wasn't going to show. Zoe supposed men like that received invitations to parties all the time. They couldn't go to all of them. Still, Drake was going to be disappointed which didn't augur well for his mood later on.

When the doorbell rang again just after ten, Zoe hoped it was this Mitch fellow and hurried to answer it, sipping her third glass of wine as she went. She swept open the door just as she was lifting her glass to her lips once more.

But it wasn't the missing Mitch. It was Aiden standing there, looking even more handsome than she remembered. He was clean shaven for starters and dressed beautifully in fawn chinos and a crisp blue shirt the color of his eyes.

Zoe's eyes rounded at the sight of him. Her mouth gaped. Her hand froze.

All coherent thought fled.

11

AIDEN knew, the moment he saw Zoe again, why he'd finally given in and come to Sydney. Just the sight of her took his breath away.

But the shock on her face brought home to him that she hadn't expected to see him again. She thought he'd been safely consigned to the closet, a spur-of-the-moment indiscretion which she didn't want to think of ever again.

Facing the cold hard reality that he'd meant nothing more to her than a one-night stand pained Aiden more than he could ever have envisaged. But at least he had answers to his questions now. If nothing else, this trip to Sydney had stopped any stupid fantasy that there was something special between them, or—as his romantic-minded mother would have put it—that Zoe might have been his one true love.

To think he'd even begun considering such a silly idea!

The shock on Zoe's face swiftly changed to a panicky confusion. "I...I never imagined for a moment that you'd follow me," she babbled. "I didn't think you'd care. But...how on earth did you know I'd be *here?* I mean...there's no way that...oh...oh, I see...you found out through Nigel, didn't you? He told you about me and Drake.'' Her big brown eyes suddenly widened with alarm. ''You're not going to tell Drake about last Saturday night, are you?''

Fear over having her own unfaithfulness exposed showed Aiden that Zoe's first priority in life was still the boyfriend.

Which again begged the question of why? Love? Or money?

Aiden was finding it harder and harder to believe it was love. Drake might be a super-successful salesman—and reasonably good-looking—but he was also a major sleazebag, as Nigel had accurately judged. Aiden hadn't needed more than an hour with the man himself this afternoon to prove that. The lewd way Drake had flirted with the receptionist at his office had been a real eye-opener. If that blonde at the conference was the first female he'd two-timed Zoe with, Aiden would eat his hat.

But then...maybe Zoe already knew that. Maybe she'd decided to turn a blind eye to Drake's extracurricular activities in exchange for what he could give her.

Not for the first time, Aiden speculated that perhaps when Zoe found out how well heeled *he* was, maybe she'd change her priorities. It was telling that having seen her again, he no longer held the high moral ground that he would not become involved with another materialistic fortune-hunting woman. As his eyes swept over Zoe in that delicious dress and his body lurched into that unable-to-be-ignored-or-subdued hard-on which had tormented him all week, Aiden realized that he would do whatever it took to have sex with her again. He'd make any compromise. Play any role she fancied. Give her anything she wanted.

"No, I'm not going to tell Drake about us," he promised, since doing so would hardly endear him to her. "So there's no need to worry. But the thing is, Zoe, I'm not exactly..."

"Mitch!" Drake interrupted before Aiden could enlighten Zoe of his identity and financial status. "So you came after all. And you're already trying to chat up my girl. Shame on you!"

"This is *Mitch?*" Zoe exclaimed, clearly stunned. "The same Mitch you were telling me about earlier on?"

"The one and only," Drake confirmed, sliding a possessive arm around Zoe's slender waist and pulling her close. "Why, darling? Who did you think he was?"

"He introduced himself as Aiden," she said coldly.

Aiden wondered what on earth Drake had told her about him to produce such contempt in her eyes.

"Mitch is a nickname I had back in my surfing days," he hastened to tell her. "But Aiden is my real name. Aiden Mitchell." He didn't want her thinking he'd lied to her about everything. Only his owning the weekender.

"Mitch suits you better," Drake insisted.

"If you'll excuse me," Zoe said brusquely. "I have food to get out of the refrigerator or it'll be too chilled for supper. I'm sure you two boys have plenty to talk about."

Aiden could have kicked himself as he watched her

walk off. Hell, he'd handled this all wrong. He should never have accepted Drake's invitation and come here tonight. It was a tactical mistake.

Why hadn't he foreseen how annoyed Zoe would be when she found out who he really was? No one liked to be made a fool of. It just showed you what happened when men started thinking with their bodies instead of their brains. Off goes your head and on goes a pumpkin!

''Don't worry about Zoe,'' Drake said, waving Aiden inside and shutting the door behind them. ''She's in a bit of a mood tonight. Been like it all week.''

Now *that,* Aiden liked to hear. It meant that maybe Zoe *hadn't* been able to dismiss him, or last Saturday night, so easily from her mind. Maybe she'd been thinking about him, too.

''Come on, Mitch, I'll get you a drink.'' Drake led Aiden down some steps into the reasonably crowded living room and over to a side table on which stood a wide array of liquor and a selection of clean glasses. ''What's your poison? You look like a Scotch on the rocks man.'' He reached for a decanter.

''A light beer would do fine. I never drink hard liquor. A habit from my surfing days.''

Drake's hand lifted from the decanter. ''Really? I'm surprised. Come over here to the bar then. I've got all kinds of beer chilling in the bar fridge. Hi, Alex, Babs,'' he said to a couple in a dimly lit corner who might have been dancing, or indulging in some foreplay. It was hard to tell which. They were certainly kissing. ''Having fun? Great. Change the music if you like.'' A sultry blues number was playing in the background.

''We already did,'' they chorused back, briefly coming up for air.

The bar was a built-into-the-construction corner, with a gray marble top and stainless-steel stools, reflective of all the furniture which was minimalist and cold-looking.

''Take a seat,'' Drake offered, waving toward the stools.

Aiden decided to stand. Drake extracted a can of light beer, zapped open the top and poured it into a glass. ''I thought surfers were supposed to be a pretty wild bunch, especially with the booze and the broads.''

''I discovered fairly early on that a hangover wasn't conducive to good form on the board.'' He accepted the beer and took a small swallow, wondering all the while how he was going to get rid of this creep and go explain things to Zoe.

''What about the women?'' Drake persisted. ''Don't tell me you were one of those dedicated athletes who abstained from sex before competition for fear it would drain all your energy away!''

''Can't say I ever subscribed to that particular theory,'' Aiden said dryly, and Drake laughed.

''Same here. I find sex the most invigorating activity. Sometimes, with the right girl, the more I have, the more I want.''

Aiden felt sick with jealousy at this revelation, 'til he realized Drake might not be talking about Zoe.

''Well, you do have one very pretty girlfriend,'' he remarked leadingly.

''What? Oh, yeah, Zoe's pretty enough. But to be honest, she's a bit on the prissy side when it comes to sex.''

''Oh?'' Aiden had considerable difficulty hiding his shock. There'd been nothing prissy about Zoe the other night. Not once she got going.

''You know what it's like. You're a man of the world.'' Drake dropped his voice to a conspiratorial whisper. ''Some women like their sex all sweet and sugar-coated. Others like it any time, any place, any way. I figured out when I was just a lad that the first kind are for marrying, and the others are just for screwing.''

''I presume the blonde at your office today is just for screwing then,'' Aiden said dryly. ''What was her name? Tracy something or other?''

''Hey, man. Hush up. We don't want Zoe hearing anything like that. Not only that, would you believe Tracy's here tonight? Turned up unexpectedly with one of my colleagues. I nearly died. Talk about living dangerously. Luckily, I've been able to avoid her all evening.''

''I think your luck might have just run out,'' Aiden said, glancing over Drake's shoulder through the archway which led into the room beyond. ''Because your blonde's heading this way. She's all alone and she looks like she's been drinking.''

''Oh, no! Do me a favor, will you, Mitch? Go and keep Zoe busy out in the kitchen while I get Tracy out of here.''

''Are you quite sure you want me to do that?'' Aiden drawled. ''Let me warn you right here and now that, unlike your blonde, I find your Zoe extremely attractive.''

Drake laughed. ''That's all right, mate. I'd trust Zoe with the most handsome man in the world, and much as you scrub up pretty well, I don't think you're in that league. But go do your best, buddy, if it'll amuse you and keep Zoe busy. But you won't even get to first base. Ah...Trace, honey, I've been wanting to talk to you all evening.''

Aiden didn't hear what Trace honey had to say in return. He was already heading for the kitchen, wherever the darned kitchen was. This was one large apartment, with the first living room spilling into a second and a third, all of them chock-full of trendily dressed yuppie types with scantily dressed women on their arms, a couple of which gave him the eye as he weaved his way past.

It amazed him that there'd been a time when he found parties like this fun. Now, he thought them boring and pretentious.

He finally found the kitchen, a long galley-style room with a white-tiled floor, gray-marble benchtops and stainless-steel appliances. Aiden thought it looked as soulless as its owner.

Zoe was standing at a far counter next to a huge two-door, stainless-steel refrigerator, peeling plastic wrap off some serving plates and muttering away to herself. She stopped briefly to refill her glass with the bottle of Chardonnay in the fridge door, taking a good gulp before going back to her work. She didn't see or hear him enter. Her back was to him. Her very pretty back.

He closed the door softly and walked toward her. She must have finally sensed something because she suddenly whirled 'round, her lovely eyes widening.

"Don't you dare touch me," she choked out. "I...I'll scream if you do."

"I haven't come in here to touch you. I just want to talk to you."

"I have nothing to say to you."

"Well, I have plenty to say to you. I don't know what Drake told you about me. I dare say something about my court case last year, judging by your negative reaction to me tonight. I just want you to hear my version."

"Now why would I want to hear *your* version?" she snapped. "I think I've already heard enough lies from you."

"I never lied to you, except over the ownership of the house up at Hideaway Beach. Everything else I told you was true."

"Which wasn't much, if you recall. You let me think you were some kind of beach bum."

"I would have told you the complete story the next morning, if you'd stayed."

"Oh, come on now, you expect me to believe that?"

"I'm hoping you will."

"Why?"

His eyes locked onto hers. "Because what we shared the other night was remarkable, Zoe. And it wasn't just the sex, though that was great, too. There was something else. Something…special. I think we owe it to each other to explore our relationship further.''

Aiden was sure that he had her there for a moment. Her eyes had gone all dreamy. But then she snapped out of it, and the contempt was back. ''Might I remind you that I'm already in a relationship, with a man I love?''

''That's trash and you know it. Whatever it is you two have together it's not love.''

''You know nothing at all about Drake and me!'' she protested fiercely.

''I know more than you realize. For starters, I know your boyfriend's a two-timing sleazebag.''

''I see,'' she bit out. ''Nigel *has* been talking, hasn't he? Okay, so Drake cheated on me. Once. He said he was sorry and I forgave him.''

''*Once?* Oh, come on now.''

She flushed a little and Aiden could see even she didn't really believe that.

''Who are you to judge another man's morals, anyway?'' she threw at him. ''If anyone's the sleazebag around here it's you.''

''I've never cheated on a girlfriend in my life.''

''No, you don't keep them around long enough. You dump them as soon as you've had enough of them. And when they won't stay dumped, you pay them off. That's the sort of man you are. A prize catch. A prince. Why on earth would I choose you over Drake?''

Aiden was getting angry. And competitive. When Aiden got angry and competitive, he often forgot the rules. Forgot to be nice. It was win at all costs. His eyes narrowed and his blood began to run red-hot.

"You can't have forgotten last Saturday night that quickly," he brought up ruthlessly. "Do I have to remind you how many times you came? How you cried out for me to do it again, even begged me on occasion? You couldn't get enough. You only ran away because you were scared to stay, you liked it that much. You know in your heart of hearts you want more of the same. If for no other reason, you should choose me for the sex. Because let's face it, sweetheart, sex between you and dear old Drake isn't anything to write home about."

She paled. "How...how could you possibly know that?"

"You were too surprised by how it felt with me inside you. It was almost like you were a virgin."

Now she blushed. Like a virgin.

"There's more to a relationship than just sex," she pointed out agitatedly.

"Tell that to the geriatrics!"

"You're not what I want," she cried.

"Don't be ridiculous. I *am* what you want. I can see it in your eyes." Which was true. Her voice was saying one thing but her eyes were telling him a different story. The contempt was gone, replaced by an anguished longing.

Aiden couldn't resist anymore. He had to touch her. Had to kiss her.

"Zoe," he groaned, and pulled her into his arms.

12

FOR a few foolishly mindless moments, Zoe sank against him and let his lips crush hers, let his tongue slide deep, and then deeper, into her mouth.

The excitement was instant, and overpowering, her mind floundering whilst her flesh wallowed in his kiss, and then his touch. Her head whirled when his hands slid down over her behind, squeezing through the silk and pressing her hard against him so that she could feel his erection.

Only someone opening the kitchen door saved her from the humiliation of losing it totally, right then and there.

''Oops. Sorry. Thought this was the little men's room.'' A male voice. Slightly slurred. ''Don't mind me. I'm outa here.''

The momentary interruption thankfully jerked Aiden's mouth up from hers and propelled Zoe back to some measure of sanity. When he tried to resume kissing her, she wrenched her mouth to one side. ''No,'' she said, and was impressed at how firm she sounded, considering her body had gone to mush. ''Let me go, Aiden.''

''You don't mean that.''

''Yes, I do. If you don't let me go, I'll scream my head off.''

His arms dropped away, his face mirroring utter shock. ''But why, for pity's sake? Didn't I just prove to you that's it me you want, not Drake?''

Zoe shook her head at his obvious bewilderment. ''Haven't you been listening to me at all? Okay, yes, so you can turn me on. But that's just sex. I want more from a boyfriend than just sex. Drake gives me more.''

''More what?'' Aiden growled. ''More money? More five-star restaurants? More fancy clothes?'' His eyes raked over her designer dress and she colored guiltily.

''So that's it,'' he said, his handsome face hardening. ''Why didn't you say so, sweetheart? You want the high life? I can give you the high life. I can give you anything you want. Just name it and it's yours. I'll deck you out in diamonds. Buy you a whole new wardrobe. Take you on a world trip. Believe me, I can afford to give you a lot more than your present boyfriend.''

She blinked her own shock at him. He really must want to have sex with her again very badly. ''I don't know whether to be flattered or insulted,'' she said, shaking her head at him. ''Either way, the answer's still no. I'm not for sale. Now please go. And don't come back. I'd also appreciate it if you'd buy your penthouse from some other agent. Drake doesn't need to do business with someone as morally deficient as you, Mr. Mitchell.''

''Morally deficient! You call *me* morally deficient? I'll have you know that...that...that...''

The phone rang, putting a merciful end to Aiden's blustering. Zoe swept over to answer it, glad to have a legitimate reason not to witness his ridiculous outrage. Anyone would think he was genuinely offended by what she'd just said. Which was crazy. The man must know what he was. A sleazy opportunist. A sexual predator. A man without honor or decency. He had no compunction about trying to seduce another man's girlfriend right under his nose. And then, when that didn't work, thought nothing of trying to corrupt her with offers of money and gifts, like she was some kind of professional mistress for hire to the highest bidder!

She snatched the receiver up from its cradle and deliberately turned her back on him. ''Yes?'' she said sharply.

''Zoe. I'm so glad you answered.''

''Mel! What are doing ringing me here at this hour? Are you in some kind of trouble? Jonathon didn't get out of line, did he?'' Mel had gone out with her new boyfriend that night. Considering what had just happened, Zoe's faith in the behavior of millionaire playboy types had plummeted to less than zero.

''No. Nothing like that. He's been a perfect gentleman. Unfortunately,'' Mel muttered under her breath. ''The thing is, Zoe, when we came back to our place for coffee after dinner, the light on the answering machine was blinking, so I ran the tape and it was Betty, wanting you to ring her at home, no matter when you got in. She mentioned some kind of emergency but didn't say what, so I rang her.''

''Oh, no, it's not Dad, is it?'' Zoe's father was in his fifties and not a man who looked after himself, healthwise. Betty had bullied him into going to the doctor last year and his cholesterol reading was sky-high. Too many dairy products in his diet, he was told. Betty had done her best to make sure he ate more sensibly, but Bill was a stubborn man, and didn't take kindly to advice, or change.

''He hasn't had a heart attack, has he?'' Zoe choked out, feeling quite nauseous.

''No, nothing like that,'' Mel said, and Zoe heaved a huge sigh of relief.

''Your dad slipped over while hosing down the milking shed this afternoon and broke his ankle, so won't be able to do the milking in the morning. Betty says that's one job she never learned to do. She says she can probably find someone local to come in and do it by tomorrow afternoon, but it's a bit hard to find anyone at this time on a Saturday night. She knows she's asking a lot but was wondering if you could drive down tonight and do it in the morning. Apparently, your father is quite confident you could do it single-handed and blindfolded.''

Zoe laughed. ''Wow. Do you realize that was almost a compliment? From my dad, no less?'' Zoe's relationship with her father was very strained. He never seemed to approve of anything she did since her decision to leave home and come to Sydney. He was always criticizing her for her choice of job, choice of lifestyle and especially her choice of boyfriend. She'd taken Drake home at Christmas and he hadn't gone down well at all.

''Too full of himself,'' his father had pronounced the day she was to go back to Sydney.

''I know what you mean,'' Mel said dryly. ''If my father ever gives me a compliment, I'll faint dead away.''

''I feel a little faint myself at the moment,'' Zoe said ruefully. ''I'm also well over the limit. I'll have to find someone to drive me home.''

''Gee, Zoe, I can't. And neither can Jonathon. We downed two bottles of claret between us over dinner. I was trying to get him tipsy so that I could have my wicked way with him. I'm so sorry. You know I would if I could.''

''No sweat. I'll find someone else. I can always ask Drake. He'll be as sober as a judge. He never drinks at these parties 'til everyone goes home.''

''He won't mind?''

''He probably will, but I'm sure he'll still do it, if I ask nicely. Anyway, thanks for calling, Mel. I'll ring Betty straight away, and tell her I'll be on my way shortly.'' She glanced up at the wall clock. It was half past ten. Home was almost a three-hour drive from here. Even if she got away at eleven, it would be nearly two by the time she arrived. Then she'd have to be up at dawn for the milking. It was going to be a long day tomorrow. Still, when family called on you in a crisis, you went. That was what family was all about, even if your father was a picky, persnickety pain.

''Ring me tomorrow and let me know what happened,'' Mel said.

''I'll do that. 'Bye.''

Zoe called her home number straight away.

Betty was over the moon at her coming to the rescue, but when she started raving on about what a wonderful girl Zoe was and how much they'd both missed her, Zoe cut the conversation short.

''Must go, Betty. I'll see you hopefully around two.'' She hung up, and just stood there, gnawing at her bottom lip. Drake was not going to be pleased. Pity she hadn't been nicer to him earlier.

''I'll drive you.''

Zoe whirled at Aiden's voice. She'd almost forgotten he was there. But only almost. She'd been doing her best to ignore him, and to pretend that her body wasn't still zinging with his kisses.

Naturally, she was tempted to say yes to his offer. Aiden Mitchell was just one big bag of temptation. And he knew it.

It was time, Zoe decided tartly, for another female to dent his massive male ego.

''Are you *still* here?'' she flung at him. ''I would have thought you'd have been well gone by now.''

''I'm not going anywhere, unless it's with you.''

''Oh, for heaven's sake, get a life!'' She stalked out of the kitchen and went looking for Drake. Her frustration level soared when she couldn't find him anywhere. No one seemed to have seen him for a while. Bob said he'd spotted him by the bar talking to Tracy about fifteen minutes earlier.

''Maybe he's gone to the bathroom,'' someone else

suggested, and she hurried down the corridor which led to the master bedroom. Drake always used his en suite bathroom on these occasions. His room was one area of the apartment he kept off-limits during his parties.

The bedroom door was shut and Zoe reached for the knob.

"Are you sure you want to go in there without knocking first?"

Zoe's head whipped 'round to find Aiden standing a few feet down the corridor, watching her.

"Will you mind your own business?" she snapped.

"I am. *You're* my business. You're why I came to Sydney and why I came to this party. Look, I apologize for the things I said to you in the kitchen. I never did really think you were the kind of girl who could be bought. I guess I was just hoping you were," he added ruefully.

"Sorry I couldn't oblige. But we're not far from the Cross here. You'll find plenty of what you're looking for up there."

"I don't want just sex, Zoe. I just want sex with you."

She rolled her eyes in exasperation. "Oh, please, *spare* me." And she started to turn the doorknob.

"I'm trying to. Don't go in there, Zoe," he warned.

Her hand stopped momentarily. "Why?"

"A workmate of Drake's named Bob just told me he hasn't been able to find his date, either. She's the receptionist at their office, name of Tracy. Blond. Big boobs."

Zoe's frustration with him finally exploded into

fury. ''If I were a man, I'd flatten you for what you just implied.''

''You're welcome to, after I'm proven wrong.''

Zoe glared at him, then flung the door open without knocking.

The room was empty.

''He's not in here,'' she informed Aiden tartly. ''Neither is Tracy. Come and see for yourself.''

He did, glancing around the room with those beautiful blue eyes of his. They landed on the en suite door which was also shut.

''I think it's time *you* saw for *yourself,*'' he ground out, and began to stride across the room.

''No, don't,'' Zoe croaked, and ran after him, fear suddenly filling her at what was behind that closed door.

But Aiden was too quick for her. He didn't knock. He didn't give anyone inside any warning. He brought up his foot and kicked the door open.

Drake squawked, his head jerking up to stare with horrified eyes at his unwanted intruders. Tracy's blond head didn't lift at first. She kept on doing what she was doing for several ghastly seconds, testament either to her drunkenness, or her dedication to finishing what she had started. But even when she did stop, she didn't seem at all embarrassed at what she'd been doing, or the fact that she was on her knees and stark naked to the waist.

She stood up and ever so slowly pulled her black lacy top back up over her large dark-tipped breasts, smiling a smug little smile as she tied it around her neck. ''Oops,'' she said mockingly.

Zoe felt like she was in the middle of a farce as she watched Drake frantically stuffing himself back into his pants.

If nothing else, the whole sordid scenario proved one thing to her.

She didn't love Drake anymore. She didn't even *like* him anymore. If she had, she'd have been more surprised. And more hurt.

Frankly, her main feeling was humiliation that Aiden was standing right next to her. And that he'd been right. Drake *was* a two-timing sleazebag.

The cynical thought came to her that it probably took one to know one.

Zoe felt such a fool.

"Zoe," Drake groaned pleadingly, his face red as a beetroot.

"Yes, I know," she returned coldly. "It was just sex." She turned to face Aiden. "Your offer still open? As a driver only, that is," she added curtly.

"Of course."

"Then let's go." Whirling, she headed for the bedroom door.

Aiden stared after Zoe for a second, not sure he liked the sudden change which had come over her. The icy toughness. The steely glint in her eye. The bitter decisiveness.

The Zoe he'd met last week was not like that.

There again, the girl he'd met last week hadn't just personally witnessed her boyfriend being pleasured by another woman.

"I don't have a car," he said, catching up with her

in the hallway. ‘‘I came in a taxi.’’ He’d left his truck at the city hotel he’d booked into earlier that day.

‘‘No problem. We’ll take my car. It’s here in the underground car-lot. I just have to get my things out of the guest room.’’

‘‘The guest room? But I thought...’’

‘‘Don’t think!’’ she snapped. ‘‘All you have to do is drive.’’ She turned into a bedroom farther along the corridor, and started shoving some clothes and toiletries in an overnight bag.

Aiden wisely kept his mouth shut after that. He didn’t want to delay her leaving in case Drake reappeared and tried to stop her. Though goodness knew what that lowlife could say to excuse his behavior this time. He could hardly use the old it-was-only-the-once line again. Maybe he’d try some new male line, like Zoe hadn’t been giving him enough and he was desperate.

Aiden raised his eyebrows at this last thought. Maybe she hadn’t been giving him *any!* It was certainly curious that her things were in the guest room. The possibility that Zoe might not have returned to Drake’s bed this week pleased Aiden no end. But he wasn’t going to ask. He might be a fool where she was concerned but he wasn’t that much of a fool. Clearly, Zoe wasn’t in the mood for chitchat. Or confidences. Or anything else for that matter.

But give her time...

Time, Aiden had. He had all the time in the world.

13

Zoe sat, slumped in the passenger seat, her head turned toward the side window, her eyes shut. She was pretending to be asleep. She'd been pretending to be asleep since shortly after she'd explained to Aiden about the emergency, then given him directions to the farm.

She hadn't wanted to talk. All she'd wanted to do was think, something she couldn't do properly if Aiden started on at her with all that stuff about finding her special and how he'd come to Sydney just to be with her again, et cetera, et cetera, et cetera. So she kept her eyes firmly shut while she replayed the events of the evening over and over in her head, trying to make sense of them all, trying to see the truth.

At least, the truth as she saw it. She couldn't speak for anyone else. More and more Zoe realized that the only person's feelings she could ever be truly sure of in this world were her own.

Perversely, in the end, she had to concede that instead of feeling shattered, or depressed, by Drake's abominable behavior, she actually felt relieved. His doing what he did had forced *her* to do what she should have done in the beginning. Split up with him. She'd hung on to their relationship like some desperado, as though it was better to have any man, even one who cheated on her, than no man at all.

Which had been foolish of her. And rather sad.

She'd honestly thought, after Greg, that she'd stopped being foolish when it came to men.

But she hadn't at all.

Drake had made an even bigger fool of her than Greg had.

Still, Drake had fooled more people than her. Fran. Mel. Betty, even. Betty had thought him charming.

But he hadn't fooled other men. Her dad hadn't liked him one little bit, and of course, neither had Aiden.

Aiden...

Zoe scooped in a deep breath and let it out slowly.

What on earth was she going to do about Aiden?

The realization that he wasn't driving her all the way home to Moss Vale in the dead of night strictly out of the goodness of his heart did not escape Zoe. His kindness had an ulterior motive, just as his kindnesses toward her had always had an ulterior motive. His helping her when she'd fallen over, his bringing her over those eggs, and then his saving her from the ocean. Not because he was one of the good guys. All because he'd wanted to get into her pants.

When his current knight-to-the-rescue act was over, he'd expect to be rewarded as men had been expecting rewards from damsels in distress since the Dark Ages.

Oh, yes. Everything came at a price with men like Aiden Mitchell.

What annoyed Zoe most was his blatant hypocrisy.

If only he would come out and just state the bare truth without trying to dress it up with romantic frills. Why not call a spade a spade? He didn't want to explore a real relationship with her. He just wanted some more sex. That was the bottom line.

And what of your own truth, Zoe? came that taunting and devilish voice which never left her alone once Aiden entered her head. *Are you willing to embrace brutal honesty yourself? Admit it. You* want *him to demand his reward. You want him to forcibly pull you back into his arms like he did in Drake's kitchen. You want him to finish what he started before you were interrupted.*

It came to her suddenly that if that man hadn't come into the kitchen when he did, she would have ended up no better than Drake, having sex with Aiden right there where she stood, mindless of who might come in and find them actually doing it.

A shudder ricocheted down Zoe's spine and sent her sitting bolt upright, her eyes flinging open.

Aiden slanted her a concerned glance. ''Bad dream?''

''Yes,'' she said agitatedly, shaken by this thought. ''Very bad.''

''Want to tell me about it?''

''No!'' she choked out, and shuddered anew.

''Fair enough. Most bad dreams are best forgotten.''

If only they could be, she thought despairingly.

''The turn off for Bowral and Moss Vale is coming up,'' he went on. ''You woke up just in time. I wanted to ask you a few things before we get to your place. I don't want to put my foot in my mouth with your folks. Firstly, who's Mel? Your sister?"

"No, my roommate," Zoe returned crisply, happy to talk practicalities with him. "I don't have any sisters. Or any brothers for that matter."

"And Betty? Who's Betty?"

"My dad's housekeeper. He's a widower."

"She lives in, does she?"

"No. She has her own house in Moss Vale. She does stay over sometimes when she ropes Dad into playing Scrabble with her. She's mad about games and never knows when to stop. Scrabble is her latest obsession."

"She sounds a character."

"Oh, she is. She's very kind, too. I love her dearly." If it hadn't been for Betty...

"Any chance of marriage between her and your dad?"

"Lord, no. Betty's only about forty. And quite attractive. Dad's over fifty, overweight and very boring. My dad's not interested in marrying again, anyway. Mom was the only woman for him. He's been miserable and broken-hearted ever since she died."

"What a shame. Still, marriage isn't the be-all and end-all. You weren't thinking of marrying Drake before tonight, were you?"

"The last person I want to talk about in any shape or form," Zoe snapped, "is Drake."

His eyes softened on her before turning back to the road. "I can appreciate that. What happened back in Sydney couldn't have been pleasant for you. But at least you now know that he didn't love you."

"No kidding." She certainly didn't need him to tell her that.

"You don't still think you love him, do you?"

Zoe sighed. "I'm not going to get into one of these conversations, Aiden. I'm far too tired and far too fed up."

"Fair enough. I'll put it on the back burner for now. But don't go thinking I won't come back to it tomorrow. I want to know all about you, Zoe. What you think. What you feel. What you want. I haven't come all this way to be fobbed off. We have unfinished business, you and I. I aim to finish it, one way or another."

Zoe was rattled by such tunnel-vision focus. She speculated for a minute or two if he could possibly be sincere. But then her recently hard-earned cynicism kicked in and she remembered that such flattering talk was only a ploy. He didn't really want to know everything about her. Talking was just a means to an end. And the end was more sex.

But she did wonder what it was about sex with her he found so compelling and addictive that he would work this hard for it. It wasn't as though he hadn't had oodles of sex before, unlike herself.

Perhaps a clue lay in his comment that she'd been like a virgin with him, constantly surprised by her feelings and responses, not to mention all those mind-blowing orgasms.

Maybe he'd really liked that. Maybe, over the years, he'd had so much sex with so many wildly experienced and uninhibited women that he found her relative innocence and inexperience refreshing.

Maybe that was what he meant by special. Maybe what appealed to him was the idea of surprising her a lot more, of introducing her to all those erotic delights she'd not yet tasted. Things such as she'd seen tonight in Drake's en suite.

Zoe wasn't sure if that prospect appalled, or enthralled her. The image popped into her mind of herself on her knees in front of Aiden, not just half naked but totally in the nude. In her mind's eye, he was nude too, his hands in her hair, his eyes downcast as he watched her, watched her doing that to him, watched her take him right to the edge. And beyond.

Zoe swallowed convulsively at the thought, a wave of heat washing through her.

"Zoe?"

"Yes," she choked out.

"We're coming into Moss Vale. Where do we go from here?"

Where indeed? she thought frantically, then gave him directions.

The farm was only a few miles the other side of Moss Vale, a hundred hectares of prime dairy country. The land was mostly river flats surrounding one large hill on which perched the old farmhouse. It was wooden and once was white, with a high-pitched, rust-red iron roof and a wide porch all the way around. A peeling picket fence enclosed the garden and kept out the cows, but the backyard was nothing like when Zoe's mom had been alive.

Zoe sometimes found it hard to look at the now-bland shrub-filled beds which lined the front fence and which had once held glorious displays of Iceland poppies and primulas and snapdragons.

Aiden pulled up outside that same front fence just as the clock on the dash clicked over to two. Before he'd even turned off the engine, Betty burst through the screen door, her short coppery hair glowing under the porch light, her smile warm and welcoming as she hurried down the path and out through the gate.

Zoe opened the passenger door and smiled up at the woman who'd saved her when she'd really needed saving. Dear Betty. Zoe loved her almost as much as she'd loved her mom.

''Hi,'' she said, climbing out of the car and reaching up on tiptoe to kiss Betty who was very tall. Just on six feet. Betty had once explained that the reason she'd never married was her height, saying with an amused twinkle in her fine gray eyes that she'd never found a boyfriend she could look up to. Zoe reckoned it was because she was far too strong-minded and independent to fancy marriage.

''You needn't have stayed up, you know,'' Zoe added. ''I could have managed.''

''Oh, as if I could go to bed. I was too excited at seeing you again. Hey, look at you!'' Betty exclaimed, taking Zoe's hands and holding them out wide so that she could better see her dress. ''Don't you look pretty in pink. But I do feel terrible at having to drag you and Drake away from your party.'' She bent down to peer into the car where Aiden was still sitting. ''Drake, I...''

She stopped on seeing it wasn't Drake behind the wheel, blinking her confusion at Zoe.

"Betty, this is Aiden," Zoe introduced with an almost weary resignation in her voice. "Aiden, this is Betty."

Aiden climbed out of the car as well. "Hi, Betty," he said cheerily across the hood. "Pleased to meet you. And before you jump to any conclusions. Zoe and I are just good friends."

Betty laughed. "With your looks? I find that hard to believe, and so will Zoe's dad. What happened to Drake?"

"Drake who?" Zoe said with a poker face.

Betty's eyebrows lifted. "Oh, I see. Like that, is it? What did he do? Refuse to drive you down here?"

"I didn't ask him. We're finished."

"Ah, well, no loss, love. If it's any consolation, I never liked him any more than your father did."

Zoe was taken aback. "But...but you said he was charming?"

"And so he was. But it was all surface charm. He had no depth."

"You can say that again," came Aiden's rueful remark.

Zoe whirled on him. "Excuse me, but I think that's the pot calling the kettle black, don't you?" She turned back to Betty. "Sorry, Betty. You know how it is with friends sometimes. Down deep, they love each other, but they fight a lot."

"I know what you mean. Your father and I don't see eye to eye on many an occasion."

"How is Dad, by the way?" Zoe asked. "How long will he be out of action?"

"Weeks. But he'll live. After you called and I gave

him the good news, he finally agreed to take the pain-killers the doctor prescribed and he's fast asleep. But come tomorrow, I want you to try and talk some sense to him. You and I both know, Zoe, that this dairy farm is no longer a going concern. Your father can only afford to keep running it because he inherited some money a few years back. But it's time he sold. He's no longer enjoying it and he's had a good offer from one of those multi-national agricultural companies. I have a feeling he might not want to sell because he thinks you're attached to the place."

"Me?" She'd always hated the farm. "I can't see why he'd think that."

"I'm not sure. Perhaps because of your mom. He says the backyard holds precious memories of her for you."

"Oh. Oh, I see..." Zoe had never told her dad, but her mom had never liked the farm. Or the house. Never. She'd just put up with it because she loved her husband. The backyard had been her only pleasure. But without her mother in it, the backyard held no precious memories for Zoe.

"I'll see what I can do," she said.

Betty smiled. "I knew I could count on you. Sensible girl, our Zoe, isn't she?" she directed at Aiden.

"Mmm," he said, and Zoe heard sarcasm in there somewhere.

"But where would Dad live?" Zoe asked, suddenly terrified that he might want to come to Sydney and live with her.

Betty shrugged. "I dare say in Moss Vale. He

wouldn't want to move away from the area, and all his friends.''

''Friends! Dad doesn't have *any* friends other than you.''

Betty gave her a reproving look. ''You'd be surprised, missy. Your dad has become quite a popular man down at the bowling club lately.''

''Dad? Popular? At a club? I don't believe it. He never goes to clubs.''

''Maybe he didn't once, but he does now. I got fed up with his moping around the place after you left at Christmas and dragged him down there myself. He had such a great time, he's joined up. Done him the world of good. Found a personality he didn't know he had. Pity about his ankle, though. I was going to take him to a decent hairdresser this week, then on to the menswear store to buy some new clothes. I guess that'll have to wait now.''

Zoe had to smile. Betty had this compulsion, it seemed, for making over ugly ducklings into swans. She might have achieved amazing things with one very fat teenage girl a few years back, but bringing an old fogey like her dad up to date would take a minor miracle. Trendy, he would never be. Still, fancy his agreeing to go to a club. And making new friends, no less. Wonders of the world would never cease!

''But enough of that,'' Betty said. ''I'm sure you two could do with a cup of tea and something to eat after your long drive. I have some fresh blueberry muffins just out of the oven.''

''Fantastic!'' Aiden exclaimed, rubbing his hands together in pleasurable anticipation. ''I'm starving.''

"You shouldn't have, Betty," Zoe chided.

"Had to do something to keep awake. Hard to play Scrabble with myself. You wouldn't happen to play Scrabble, would you, Aiden?"

"Do I play Scrabble! I happen to be the resident Shelley Bay champion. But I'm even more famous for the number of hot muffins I can devour in one sitting. So lead me to the kitchen immediately, Betty. But come tomorrow, look out. I show no mercy when it comes to games."

Zoe had a feeling he showed no mercy in lots of things. He was a winner through and through, which was possibly another reason why he'd chased after her to Sydney. Because he didn't like the fact *she'd* made the decision last weekend to leave things at a one-night stand. Clearly, he liked calling the shots where his sex life was concerned. *He* decided when enough was enough.

"Coming, Zoe?" he said, taking her arm. Betty was already on her way up the front path.

Zoe stared down at his long strong fingers then up into his far too handsome face.

"I need my bag," she said stiffly and extracted her arm from his, turning away to collect her things from the back seat of the car.

"Let me carry it," he offered.

"No, thanks," she said crisply. "Letting you carry my things is what got me into trouble in the first place."

He frowned. "You think I'm trouble?"

"I *know* you're trouble."

"Mmm. And what do you think you are to me?"

“A challenge.”

He frowned, then nodded. “I never thought of you in that light before, but you could be right. I do like a challenge.”

“Either that, or a titillation for your jaded sexual palate.”

His eyebrows shot up. “A titillation!”

“Yes. You think you can teach me a thing or two.”

His surprised expression slowly changed to intrigued. “And can I?”

“Undoubtedly,” came her droll remark.

“But will you let me?”

She stared straight at him. “Not if I can help it.”

“Why not?”

“Because I don’t want to get hurt.”

“Are you two coming inside?” Betty called from where she was holding open the screen door.

“We’re on our way,” Aiden returned.

“I won’t hurt you,” he claimed as he took her arm and propelled her through the gate. “I promise. I won’t do a single thing you don’t want me to do.”

She laughed. Because that was the problem. There wasn’t *anything* she didn’t want him to do.

14

"HERE," Zoe said, handing Aiden a hose. "You can help with the cleaning up. All the concrete areas in the milking shed have to be hosed down."

Aiden gave her a look of mock surprise. "You mean you actually trust me to *do* something, instead of just stand around like a useless lump while you do everything?"

Zoe shrugged, determined not to bite. "Sometimes it's quicker to do everything yourself than to explain things to someone else. It's not as though you're ever going to be milking cows again, are you?"

"I guess not."

"I did tell you I didn't need your assistance," she reminded him tartly. "But you wouldn't listen. You had to play Mr. Macho Helping Hand. You could have still been in bed, sleeping."

"And miss watching you work in that highly original but incredibly sexy little outfit?"

Zoe winced. She'd been forced to wear the short shorts and top she'd been wearing the previous day before the party, since that was all she'd brought down with her and all her old clothes were miles too large. No way was she ever going to let Aiden see how fat she'd once been, by donning any of those awful baggy things she'd once worn.

The shorts did look a bit risky, however, when combined with knee-high black rubber boots.

Zoe had been fiercely aware of Aiden ogling her backside every time she had to bend over to attach or detach the cups from the cows' udders. She'd pretended not to notice, and also pretended to herself that the beads of perspiration on her forehead were courtesy of the summer sun, and not her traitorous body being revved up by Aiden's presence once more.

"I had nothing else to wear," she snapped. "You're lucky that some of Dad's old things fitted you. Now stop trying to get a rise out of me and start hosing everything down."

"If you insist." Without any warning, he turned on the nozzle and directed the spray straight at her. She squealed, her hands flying up to protect herself, waving frantically from side to side.

Thankfully, the water wasn't cold. It was actually very warm from where the hose had been lying in the sun. But it was still wet, the hot stream quickly soaking her minimal clothes.

"Stop that!" she screamed.

When he didn't stop, she spun away and ran into the first milking stall, but that didn't help at all. The spray easily found its way through the widely spaced wooden slats. She whirled back but found herself cornered, Aiden having moved to block her path, still spraying her with water, and grinning his head off. By this time her hair hung soggily around her face and her top was plastered to her skin.

''Stop it, Aiden,'' she choked out, spitting one long strand of lank hair out of her mouth.

He laughed. ''Never. Not 'til you beg for mercy.''

One part of her wanted to laugh back, to play physical games with him as was natural for men and women when in the grip of a fierce sexual attraction.

But she couldn't find the courage to let herself relax with him in such a fashion. If she did, she knew she was lost. Instead, she lunged for the end of the hose and tried to wrestle it away from him.

''Wait 'til I get that away from you. I'll…I'll…'

''You'll what?'' he said, calling her bluff by dropping the hose on the concrete where it weaved and danced like some water-spitting cobra.

His action took her by surprise and she just stood there, panting with exertion, her chest rising and falling. He just stood there too, staring at her, his eyes hot on her explicitly outlined breasts and shockingly erect nipples.

''Zoe,'' he said thickly, and her stomach curled over.

''No…''

''Yes,'' he insisted, his face and voice vibrating with the most seductive desire. She felt her nipples harden even further, puckering up for him in the most blatant way.

''No, I said,'' she croaked out again when his hand reached out to touch where his smouldering gaze was riveted. But it was a futile protest, and she didn't really mean it, not once he made skin contact.

She sucked in, her shoulders stiffening, not daring to move a muscle as his fingertips traced the various shapes and outline of her breasts through the wet top. Shivers ran up and down her spine, but not with cold. When she moaned and swayed on her feet, he grabbed her upper arms and spun her 'round, yanking her back against the hard warmth of his own relatively dry body. Once there, his hands were soon busy on her body once more, smoothing down over her ribs and stomach, then sliding up under her top.

She gasped when he reached her bare breasts, the sensations sharper now that there wasn't any material between him and her. She closed her eyes and tried to keep her head. But this was one of the things she'd thought about endlessly. One of the things she craved. His hands on her naked flesh once more.

"Say you'll come away with me," he whispered in her ear, one hand cupping her left breast whilst his right slid down over her stomach and dipped under the elastic waistband of her shorts.

"Take a few days off work," he urged, that knowing hand zeroing in on exactly the right spot.

Everything inside her crunched down hard.

"Tell them you want stress leave," he went on even as she began to spin out of control. "Tell them anything. Only come away with me, Zoe. This week. Back to Hideaway Beach. Promise me."

At that moment, she would have promised him anything.

"All right," she groaned. "Anything. Anything. Just don't stop."

He didn't stop, but his fingers moved on, sliding down into those parts which had been hot and wet for him all week. When his hand began to penetrate her body, her flesh contracted fiercely, gripping his fingers as she would have gripped his penis, showing him how much she wanted just that.

He muttered something but she didn't catch what. She could not concentrate on anything but her own feverish feelings and those devastating fingers. She whimpered when they began a rhythmic stroking, her legs moving restlessly apart as the pressure built and the craving grew even more intense. Desperate with desire, she began rubbing her bottom against Aiden's erection, oblivious of the reckless nature of such an action. Her brain was simply not connected with her body. She wasn't thinking of risk, or danger, just release. Her body was working on autopilot, blindly going after what it wanted and needed.

''Please,'' she started begging. ''Oh, please...''

Aiden muttered a four-letter word, and then something—his thumb pad, she guessed later—rubbed over her exquisitely sensitized clitoris.

Her climactic cries sounded liked the cries of a wounded animal. Her body stiffened then arched as spasm followed electric spasm. Finally, they ended and Zoe sagged at the knees, only Aiden's arms around her waist preventing her from sinking to the ground.

It took a while before reality returned and it was a deeply shaken Zoe who gradually began to appreciate that Aiden could have taken brutal advantage of her just then, if he'd been so inclined.

But he hadn't. Thank God.

Despite feeling mortified at her own lack of control, Zoe could not help but admire him for his. Not many men would have exercised that much control and consideration in the face of such temptation.

Or had he been looking at the bigger picture, ruthlessly exchanging one passing pleasure for the promise of many? A whole week's worth. He'd said he was merciless when it came to games.

But surely a merciless man would have demanded more from her just then. He could have made her do anything he wanted.

"You won't go back on your promise, will you?" he asked as he turned her back to face him.

She looked up into his beautiful blue eyes and saw an unexpected vulnerability. Amazing! Didn't he know how much she wanted him? Couldn't he *tell?*

As blinding as it had been, that one orgasm hadn't satisfied her cravings one bit. If anything, they were stronger than before, like an uncontrollable fire, unable to be doused, still raging and racing out of control. She couldn't look at him without wanting to strip him naked and touch him all over.

Only pride stopped her from doing just that. Pride and the desperate need to take control of her life once more. If she was going to do this—and she was—then she had to do it on *her* terms, not his.

"I won't go back on my promise," she said firmly, and he looked taken aback.

"You won't?"

"No, because it's what I want too," she said boldly. "What I need. A week of sex with you. But just sex, Aiden. Nothing else. So please...don't feel you have to fancy things up with romantic frills. I want no five-star restaurants. No sweet little gestures or gifts. Certainly no poetry or perfume or flowers,'' she scorned, thinking of Drake's tried-and-true tactics. ''But above all, none of that getting-to-know-you garbage. No deep and meaningful conversations. No confiding everything about each other since the year dot. Just sex.''

Talking, Zoe suspected, was the way to a woman's heart, not sex. Because talking led to true intimacy and emotional bonding. It was how Greg had got to her. And Drake as well. The sex hadn't done the trick at all. If she couldn't learn from her previous mistakes then she didn't deserve to be happy.

And Zoe aimed to be happy one day. She just had to get Aiden out of her system first.

''Just sex?'' he repeated, as though he'd never heard of the concept.

''Yes.'' Her chin tipped up. ''That's the deal. Take it or leave it. It's up to you.'' Now that she understood the basic nature of the male beast, Zoe had no doubts he'd take it.

''Mmm.''

''Is that a yes or a no?'' Surely he wasn't going to say no!

''This isn't some kind of revenge or rebound thing, is it? You're not just trying to go one better than Drake, or get back at him for what he did?''

''Don't be ridiculous. If I wanted anything like that I'd have told Drake about you and me when I had the chance. Believe me when I say Drake means absolutely nothing to me anymore. Tracy's welcome to him.''

''Just checking. A man does have his pride, you know.''

''Does he?'' she scoffed. ''I didn't think a man ever let his pride get in the way of a good lay.''

''Mmm.''

She did so hate those cryptic mmms.

His head cocked on one side. ''Is that what you think you are to me, Zoe? A good lay?''

''*You* must think so. Or you wouldn't be so keen.''

He laughed. ''You could be right there. And you could be wrong. But since we won't be chatting much, you'll never find out.''

''I can live with that.'' She had to. To find out more about him might be the kiss of death. He was already proving himself to be more than she'd imagined. But he was still not a man to be trusted with her heart. Zoe wasn't going to be a silly female fool a *third* time!

''Mmm.''

''Must you say mmm like that every second?''

''Does it bother you?''

''Yes!''

''Then I'll try to curtail it, but it's a family trait.''

''I don't want to hear about your family. Or your family's traits.''

''Oh. Sorry. I forgot. Silly me. So when do you think you might be ready to leave for Hideaway Beach?''

''That depends on whether Betty can get someone to do the milking this afternoon.''

''What are you going to tell them at work?''

''Don't you worry about that. That's my problem.''

"I think we should still stay down here today and tonight, regardless, Zoe. We might be needed. Besides," he added with a wicked grin. "I promised to play Scrabble with Betty, and like you, I always keep my promises."

Zoe pulled a face at him. "Yeah, right." Like he'd kept his promise to marry that girl. "We could still leave after tea," she suggested.

"And drive up the coast road at night? I don't think so. Too dangerous. We can make tracks first thing in the morning."

"Fine," she agreed offhandedly. But inside, she felt piqued by his plans. Okay, so he obviously wasn't as desperate as she was to be together. He'd already won her cooperation, hadn't he? He already had his precious week of uninterrupted sex to look forward to.

A shudder ran through her at the thought.

"Why don't you go back up to the house?" she suggested sharply. "Betty will have a lavish country-style breakfast ready for you by now. I'll stay here for a while to finish up and dry off."

He gave her one of his thoughtful looks, which were just as irritating as his cryptic mmms.

"I'd rather wait for you."

"And I'd rather you didn't."

When her hands found her hips, he shrugged. "All right. See you soon, then."

By the time Zoe started walking back up to the house almost an hour later, it was way past breakfast time. The angle of the sun in the sky suggested it was at least ten, or later. But she didn't care. She had no appetite for food. She'd lost it when Aiden came into her life, replaced by another more ravenous hunger.

Zoe still could not believe what had happened down at that milking shed. She also couldn't believe she'd rashly promised to get this week off work. She was going to have to spin a good yarn to wangle that. Maybe she could exaggerate her father's need for her. Family emergencies were often looked upon more kindly than just asking for time off out of the blue. She'd also have to give Mel a ring and give her an update. Maybe she'd use the same white lie on her, too.

It was difficult once you started having dirty little secrets in your life.

"Ho, ho, ho."

Zoe's head snapped up at the sound of her father's deep Santa-like belly laugh. She'd just come through the back gate and was only a few steps from the open back door. Surprise understated Zoe's reaction. Frankly, she hadn't heard her father laugh like that in years.

She hurried in through the screen door to find him sitting at the old kitchen table, showing an equally amused-looking Aiden an old photograph album.

Her heart sank when she immediately recognized it as one which contained all her class photos, right from her first year at school, including the dreaded ones taken after her mother had died and she'd become so fat. They were the only photographs of her taken during those awful years, and then only because the school forced her to be in them. Because she wasn't tall, she was always put in the front row, all her grossness there on open display. Not just her fat face but her fat stomach and fat legs. She'd even had fat ankles back then.

A fierce wave of humiliation seared her soul as Aiden looked up, a wide smile on his face.

"You sure were a cute little..."

"How dare you show those photos of me without my permission!" she raged at her father, racing over and snatching the offending album out of his startled hands. Tears welled up in her eyes. "Isn't it enough that you've always put me down? Must you hold me up to ridicule in front of..."

She broke off when she realized the album she was holding wasn't the one with her school photos in. It was the one which contained her baby photos, along with the photos of her parents, when they were young and happy together. That other awful album, Zoe recalled too late, had been long consigned to a dark hiding place which only she knew about. It was just that the album covers were the same...

Everyone was staring at her with shocked eyes. Betty, standing at the sink. Her pale-faced father sitting at the table, his broken ankle propped up on a chair. Aiden, seated to the left of him.

"Oh," she cried, shattered at having made a complete idiot of herself and embarrassing everyone for nothing.

"I'm sorry," she said, and bursting into tears, she ran headlong from the room, clutching the album to her chest.

She was lying facedown on her bed, her weeping having subsided to the odd sniffle when she heard her bedroom door open. She knew without looking 'round, that it would be Betty. Dear, kind, understanding, sympathetic Betty.

"I know," she croaked into her pillow. "I behaved like an idiot."

"Not at all," a male voice answered. "I'm the one who's been behaving like an idiot all these years."

Zoe rolled over at the sound of his voice.

"Dad!"

"Yes, it's me. Not that I've been much of a dad since your mother died. And I'm sorry, Zoe. I've been abominably selfish, too caught up in my own pain to begin with to see yours. When I finally did, I didn't know how to handle you or your weight problem. Thank goodness for Betty, that's all I can say. What a godsend that woman's been."

Zoe watched, too startled to speak, as her father struggled into the room on his crutches and closed the door behind him. When she went to get up and help him, he waved her back and leaned against the dressing table for support.

"Betty just gave me a good talking to in the kitchen and made me see how critical and negative I've been toward all you've achieved. She made me see it wasn't easy for you losing weight, then getting a job and going off to the city to live all by yourself. At the time I took it as a personal rejection of me and our life here as a family. I hated the fact that you hated the farm. Much like your mom did."

Zoe's heart lurched. "I...I didn't know you knew that..."

His eyes carried admission, and true remorse.

"Once again, I pretended I didn't notice. Men are good at that. Pretending not to notice the things they don't want to face. But I knew she was unhappy, just as I knew you were unhappy."

"She still loved you, Dad. And so do I."

"I know that, daughter. And that's what makes me feel even lousier. But hopefully, it's never too late to turn things around. So I just want to say that I *am* proud of you for the success you've made of your life. I wish I had your courage. And your willpower. And your selflessness. What you did, dropping everything and driving down here in the middle of the night, puts me to shame. Not once, in the five years you've lived in Sydney have I driven up and visited you. Not once. All I've done is complain and criticize. I don't know why you still bother with me at all."

Tears welled up in Zoe's eyes again. "Oh, Dad... Thank you so much for saying that, but I'm not such a great success. Not with men, anyway. Did Betty tell you Drake did the dirty on me and I had to dump him?"

"Yes. And good riddance to bad rubbish. You've got yourself a much nicer bloke sitting out there in the kitchen, my girl. He makes ten of that Drake."

"You like Aiden?" Zoe shouldn't have been surprised. *She* liked him, didn't she?

"I sure do. He's a real nice lad. So easy to talk to. And no airs and graces about him, either, despite all his successes. He really likes you too, Zoe. And not because you're done up like a dog's dinner all the time, either. I know you told Betty you were just good friends, but you mark my words. No man would drive you all the way down here because he just wants to be good friends with you.''

''Really,'' she said, trying not to smile. But it was kind of funny.

''Yes, really, I'm a man. I know. I can see the signs.''

''Speaking of signs, Dad, I've been seeing a few signs myself between you and Betty. Am I right or am I wrong or are you two more than just good friends these days?''

He blushed. He actually blushed.

''No need to feel embarrassed, Dad,'' Zoe raced on. ''I'm not shocked,'' she lied. ''You're a grown man just as she's a grown woman. You can do exactly as you please behind closed doors. But if you want my daughterly advice I think you should sell the farm, move into Moss Vale and marry Betty.''

''You think she'd actually *marry* me?'' It was rather touching that he looked so unsure.

Zoe looked her dad over and tried to see him through Betty's older eyes. He'd once been a handsome man and would still be, if he lost some weight, bought himself some new clothes and had his hair cut. There was nothing worse than a man who was going bald who grew what was left of his hair longer, thinking that made up for it.

''I think she might,'' Zoe said. ''But she's a very attractive woman, Dad. Now don't get me wrong, you're still a fine figure of a man but you have let yourself go a bit. If I were you, I'd try to lose a few pounds, get your hair cut in one of those shorter more modern styles and invest in some new clothes, especially for when you take Betty down to the club. You have been taking her down to the club, haven't you?''

He nodded. ''And you think that would work?'' he asked, looking as eager as a schoolboy trying to wangle a date with the beauty of the class.

''It can't hurt. Go for it, Dad. You only have the one life to live.''

He drew himself up taller with her encouraging words. ''You're right. But none of this to Betty now. I want to do this all by myself.''

15

AIDEN sat with arms folded in the passenger seat, irritated that Zoe had insisted on driving. Like most men, he hated not being the driver.

''For pity's sake, stop sulking,'' she threw over at him as they wound their way down through cow-dotted fields toward the main road. ''It *is* my car. Which reminds me. Where is that chick-pulling yellow truck you usually drive? Or is that just part of the beach-bum role you adopt at Hideaway Beach? You leave it behind when you head for Sydney and put on your millionaire's hat again.''

Aiden slanted a thoughtful glance over at her. She really had it all wrong about him. Understandable, of course, given what she'd been told and what she'd been through with Drake this last week. Lies and betrayals always affected a person deeply. You automatically turned cynical and, yes, bitter.

Aiden had been there, done that, and he knew what Zoe was going through. All he could do was be patient and play for time, time for her to discover the real him.

''It's at the hotel I booked into in Sydney. But no sweat, it can stay there for this week. I'll give them a call and explain the situation.''

"Oh, really? You'll tell them that you're off for some serious sex with a chick with her own wheels so you won't be needing your own?"

Aiden smiled at her sarcasm. When women got sarcastic, it was often because underneath, they cared. Zoe might think she only wanted sex from him, but he was bargaining she actually wanted more, but was afraid of being hurt. She'd said as much.

For his part, he was sure now that he wanted more from Zoe than just sex. The incident yesterday morning in the milking shed had proved that. If it had been just lust driving him, he would have undoubtedly done something they'd both have regretted afterward.

But he hadn't. He'd stayed in control, wanting to give rather than take.

Okay, so he'd been a bit naughty, using her wildly turned-on state to coerce that promise from her. But as they say, all's fair in love and war.

Aiden was beginning to suspect this could develop into a bit of both.

Whatever, he knew he'd never felt this strongly about any girl before, and he wasn't about to be fobbed off with one week of sex. He aimed to have a real relationship with Zoe. She was going to become his girlfriend, come hell or high water.

In the meantime, he would give her what she wanted, or *thought* she wanted.

"My, aren't we in a touchy mood this morning?" he said lightly. "What's up?"

"You know very well what's up! Last night, over dinner, you let Betty and Dad think you were already my new boyfriend."

''Is that a crime?''

''It's a lie. You are not, and are never going to be, my new boyfriend. You're going to be my sexual partner. For one week and one week only. That was the deal. If you think you can change my mind on that, then think again, lover.''

''Fine. Don't get uptight.''

''I have every reason to get uptight. As it is, I'll be fielding off questions from Betty and Dad for ages after this is over. They *liked* you. Though of course I can understand why. You went out of your way to be so darned nice to them. Sitting there all yesterday afternoon, watching the football with Dad and drinking that awful beer he likes! Then playing Scrabble with Betty 'til all hours of the night! *And* letting her win!''

''I didn't let her win,'' Aiden said truthfully. ''She beat me fair and square. I guess I'm a bit rusty. I haven't been my hometown Scrabble champion for some few years.''

''And that's another thing. You are such a blabbermouth, telling everyone everything all about yourself. I told you I didn't want to know any of that stuff and now I do. Not that it makes any difference. Betty and Dad might have been impressed at what a success you've made of your life after starting out as the poor underprivileged son of a single mom, but you didn't fool me with your sob stories. Amongst other things, what sensible woman would refuse to take welfare, then scratch out some wretched existence selling painted scarves and sarongs to tourists?''

''My mom would,'' he said ruefully. ''Wait 'til you meet her. You'll believe me, then.''

''I have no intention of meeting your mother,'' she said stiffly. ''I told you. I don't want to get to know you or your family. All I want is for you to...to... You know what I want you to do!'' she finished, flushing prettily.

He never said a word. But he started planning a lot. She thought she knew what she was doing keeping their relationship strictly sexual, but she didn't. She was being naive again.

''Look, I don't mean to be rude,'' she went on, perhaps reading offense into his silence. ''I like you. I really do. You're a very likable person. But we had a deal. We were not supposed to have any getting-to-know-you conversations.''

''You started it, complaining about my talking to your folks back at the farm.''

''Which reminds me. Exactly what *did* you and Betty talk about after I went to bed last night? You didn't go asking her personal questions about me, did you?''

''Absolutely not,'' Aiden denied, and it wasn't a lie. He'd asked all those questions earlier in the day, after she'd run off crying to her room and her father had finally followed her.

And what an enlightenment that conversation had proved to be!

He'd already discovered for himself at Drake's party that Zoe was not some kind of cold-blooded gold digger, that she was as sweet and sincere as she'd seemed the previous weekend. But it was good to hear some solid details about Zoe's earlier life, and to work out just what had made her so susceptible to the likes of Drake Carson. Betty hadn't needed much prodding to tell Aiden everything he wanted to know about this girl who'd turned his life upside down.

He'd been saddened to hear of her mother's premature death of uterine cancer when Zoe had only been thirteen, then sympathetic when Betty explained that Zoe had spent the rest of her teenage years being "mother" around the house because her father couldn't afford help. She did all the cooking and cleaning whilst still at school, then after leaving school as well. He understood a great deal when he heard about her comfort eating which resulted in her weight ballooning out, thereby undermining her self-esteem. More pennies dropped for Aiden when Betty told him Zoe had retreated from reality into the world of women's magazines where all successful women were slim and perfectly groomed, had interesting careers and handsome boyfriends.

Two events eventually stopped the rot. Zoe contracted mononucleosis, just after her father inherited a wad of cash from an uncle who died. With it, he was able to employ Betty to look after the house and a slowly recovering Zoe.

Aiden didn't have to read between the lines to realize that Betty had brought new life into that once-depressed household. Betty had a vibrant and optimistic personality, and was so full of the joy of living, with a passion for lots of things besides Scrabble. With her encouragement, Zoe had watched her diet, started exercising, taken a secretarial course and finally applied for some jobs, not locally, but in Sydney. Successful women didn't work in the country. They had glamorous jobs in the city.

She'd taken a while but she'd finally landed a position as a clerk in an insurance company where unfortunately, some pig of a man—Betty didn't know the sordid details—hurt her rather badly. Zoe had still been a bit plump at the time so who knew what emotional scars had been inflicted on her still-vulnerable self-esteem. Quite a lot apparently, because after that, she'd steered clear of men for a good few years, choosing instead to work her way up in the world by going to more night schools and trimming off every excess pound from her figure with many more hours spent in gyms, 'til she landed her present job last year.

It had been shortly after she started her job as assistant to Fran Phillips that Drake Carson had come into her life with all his false charm and self-centered ambition.

Aiden knew exactly why Drake had targeted Zoe.

Because he saw in her the perfect wife for a man like him. She was attractive, well-groomed, hardworking. But more importantly, slightly naive, lonely and needy. Not yet life smart, despite all she'd achieved. She stood no chance against him, once he went to work with all those age-old romantic ploys designed to fool women.

Zoe herself had revealed exactly what Drake had used to suck her in when she'd told Aiden what she *didn't* want from him. Flowers. Five-star restaurants. Perfume. Poetry. Gifts of any kind.

No doubt dear old Drake had lavished all these on her at every opportunity.

There was one thing, however, which Drake had never been able to give Zoe, because it couldn't be bought, or fabricated. And that was the sort of sexual pleasure she'd experienced with *him.*

Aiden aimed to take full advantage of that. He aimed to bind Zoe to him through sex, to take her to places she'd never been before, to use physical intimacy to draw her into an emotional intimacy. There would be no taboos this coming week. No nos of any kind. He was going to make her his. Totally.

Zoe's head abruptly whipped 'round to glare over at him. ''You're being very quiet, all of a sudden,'' she said accusingly.

''Isn't that what you want?'' he returned, doing his best not to look like a man making a mental list of various wicked activities. ''No talking?''

''Huh. Don't play the innocent with me.''

He laughed. ''I wouldn't dream of it. Hey, watch the road, would you? Or let me drive.''

Zoe jerked the car back from where it had drifted toward the center line.

''Speaking of driving,'' she said. ''I think it best you take your own vehicle back up to Hideaway Beach, so I'll drop you off at your hotel in Sydney on the way through.''

''Oh, no, no, no,'' he said, sitting up straight. ''That's not on. I'm not letting you out of my sight.''

''But I have to go to my place and pick up some things.''

''Then I'll come with you.''

"But I don't want you to. Mel might be there."

"So?"

"I don't want her to know about you."

His eyes narrowed and his fists clenched. "Then I'll sit outside in your car and wait."

"No," she said stubbornly. "We'll do this my way. You'll just have to trust me. I promised to come and I will."

Aiden gritted his teeth. He supposed he had no other alternative. But this was the last time she'd treat him this shabbily. Come the end of the week, he aimed to have her eating out his hand.

"I guess I'll just have to take your word for it," he said grudgingly.

"I guess you will."

Aiden didn't like the smug tone in her voice. Maybe he'd miscalculated a little here. Maybe her earlier sarcasm hadn't been a sign of secret caring. Maybe all she *did* want from him was just sex.

The thought rattled him. Then turned him on.

He'd thought he'd worked her out there. He'd thought he'd worked *himself* out, too.

Now he didn't know where he was going or what he was doing, except for one thing. He was going to screw that girl's brains out this week. And she was going to love every single second!

16

ZOE was smiling to herself as she slipped her key into her front door. She hadn't realized the satisfaction which came from taking control of one's life, in making your own decisions and then not making any excuses for them.

She'd always been so accommodating with Drake, pandering to his ego and doing everything to please him. Even when she'd refused to move in with him, she'd been apologetic about it.

Did he respect her for that? Heck, no! He'd still thought her a pushover. And a fool. She was never going to be like that again. She was going to be more like a man in future, doing exactly what she wanted to do without saying sorry all the time.

Aiden hadn't been happy with her decision about the cars. But when she'd stood firm, he'd accepted it. She vowed to remember that in all her dealings with him. To stay firm.

''You home, Mel?'' she called out, hoping her roommate wasn't in. ''It's Zoe!''

''I'm in the bathroom!'' Mel shouted back, putting paid to that hope. ''Won't be long. Can't talk. I'm cleaning my teeth. I'll be out soon.''

At which point she would no doubt ask some sticky

questions. Like, what was she doing here? Where was she going? And why?

Zoe would have to be very inventive with her answers.

Sighing, she hurried into her room and stripped off the track suit Betty had found for her to wear that morning and which had only been bearable because of her car's air-conditioning. The weather was remaining hot and dry, despite the fact that March—and the Australian Fall—had arrived. It looked like they were in for an Indian summer.

She pulled on some loose lemon crinkle slacks which traveled well, and matched them with a white short-sleeved shirt, not tucked in. She popped her feet into strappy white sandals, and bundled her hair up into a tiny ponytail, leaving a few tendrils to soften the rounded outline of her face. Her makeup was nothing but a dash of coral lipstick.

It was not a bad look. Not one she'd wear to work but it would do for today. And for the rest of the week. Aiden was attracted to her, as her dad had noticed, whether she was dolled up or not. So why bother? It would be silly to spend hours every morning doing a full face makeup and blow-dry when she'd wasn't intending to go outside the door. For the same reason, she didn't intend to take up many clothes. She would have no call for them.

Zoe's mouth went dry as she thought of not wearing any clothes at all. All week. Of walking around in the nude all the time. Of always being accessible to him.

A violently erotic shiver ran down her spine.

''So what are you doing home?'' Mel demanded to know as soon as she walked into the room. ''I thought after your phone call last night you were going to be spending the whole week down at the farm.''

Zoe did her best to look calm and carefree, whilst every nerve ending she owned felt electrified. ''I thought so, too,'' she said, not looking at Mel as she went about collecting underwear from her drawers. ''But Betty came up with a local chap who was happy to come in and do the milking 'til Dad's on his feet again. Provided he was paid, of course. So I wasn't needed anymore.''

''I would have thought you'd still have stayed home for a while after what happened with Drake. Moral support and all that. You must have been very upset. What a creep! You did right to dump him. One slip could be forgiven, but twice? No way. So why are you dressed like that?'' she asked, flopping down on the side of Zoe's bed. ''You're obviously not going back to work.''

''Nope. I thought, since I already had the week off work, that I'd go away for a few days.''

''I'm surprised your boss agreed to you having a whole week off.''

''I was too, to be honest. Fortunately, I'd worked like a dog last week so I was more than up to date with everything. Besides, it's not as though I asked for any special favor. I took a week of the two weeks' holidays I'd already accrued.''

''You shouldn't have had to do that.''

''Maybe, but I felt better that way.'' Less guilty.

''And just as well,'' she added. ''Now I'm free to go wherever I like.''

''Well, you look beachy, so I presume you're off somewhere coastal?''

''Yes. Back to Hideaway Beach.''

''Really? I didn't think you liked it up there that much.''

''I always like the beach,'' she said, keeping busy with her packing. ''It was the timing which was wrong.''

''I dare say. Er…are you quite sure Nigel's gay?''

''What?'' Zoe glanced 'round at her friend and roommate, confused by the question. ''What do you mean?''

''I mean he's being very generous, lending you his beach house all the time. Unless it's not Nigel's place you're staying at?'' There was a hint of suspicion in that last question.

Zoe wished she was a better actor at this point. Or a better fibber.

With Mel looking straight at her, she just couldn't bring herself to lie.

''No,'' she admitted, flushing guiltily. ''No, I'm not staying at Nigel's.''

Mel's blue eyes rounded in surprise, before twinkling with salacious delight. ''You've been a naughty girl, haven't you? You did go with some lifesaver up there last week, didn't you? Go on, tell the truth and shame the devil.''

''Well…almost.''

''*Almost?* How can you *almost* go with someone?''

"No, I slept with him, all right. But he wasn't a lifesaver. He was a surfer."

"A surfer!"

"A very famous surfer, actually. His name's Aiden Mitchell and he owns the weekender next to Nigel's."

"Aiden Mitchell! Oh, my goodness, that's some surfer. I mean he was just the best! He was also on Australia's ten most eligible bachelors list a couple of years ago. I know because I cut it out and did my best to meet every one of them. But I never did come across him. He's not all that social a guy. He keeps a pretty low profile. Or he did 'til last year. You do know about his being sued by that actress, don't you?"

An actress? She hadn't known the girl involved was an actress. Zoe wasn't sure if that was in Aiden's favor or against it. An actress would make an excellent liar, unlike herself.

"I didn't when I first met him," Zoe admitted on a sigh. "I didn't recognize him at all. I thought he was just some gorgeous beach bum, living in the house next door to Nigel's while he was doing some renovation work on it. And he let me think so too, the rat. Still, what can you expect from a man like that?"

"Not an engagement ring, that's for sure. So watch your step."

"I'm not planning on marrying him, Mel. I just want to sleep with him."

"I gather you already did."

"Okay, I just want to sleep with him some more."

"That good, eh?"

"Brilliant."

"Ooh, I'm jealous. Do you know Jonathon won't go to bed with me?"

"Goodness me, why not?"

"He says he loves me too much and I'm far too cynical. He says he wants to wait so that I'll know just how *much* he loves me, that it's not just lust he feels for me."

"Well, I certainly don't have that trouble with Aiden. That's all he wants from me. Sex. And frankly, that's all I want from him."

Mel gave Zoe a worried look. "Are you sure? I mean…that doesn't sound like you."

"I know. But meeting Aiden has opened my eyes to a side of me I didn't know existed. From the moment I set eyes on him, I could think of nothing else but sex. I don't want him to love me, Mel. I just want him to…"

"Make love to you," Mel finished for her on a dry note.

Zoe laughed. "I wasn't going to put it quite like that."

"I know. And that's not like you, either. You're not that kind of girl, Zoe. I don't like the sound of this. Aiden Mitchell! Who would have believed it? Talk about going from the frying pan into the fire. That is one seriously hot-looking hunk of male flesh. And rich, to boot. Are you sure you haven't fallen for him and you just won't admit it?"

"No," Zoe said firmly. "I haven't. And I don't intend to. I'm not the same person post-Drake as I was before, Mel. I won't be giving my heart so easily in future, or so stupidly. No, it's just sex."

"Not *just* sex," Mel corrected. "*Fantastic* sex, by the sounds of things."

"True. I've never had anything like it before. And I want a whole lot more. But come next Sunday I'll be back here, I'll be alone and I'll be fine."

"Wow! I'm impressed. This is pussy power at its best. I love it."

"I rather like it, too. Now, I just have to get my toilet bag out of the bathroom and I'll be ready."

"Want me to make you a cup of coffee before you go?"

"Oh, yes, that would be nice."

Five minutes later both girls were sipping coffee in the kitchen when suddenly, Zoe's courage began to fade.

"You...you don't think I'm being reckless, do you, Mel?"

Mel gave her an exasperated look. "Now don't go spoiling the new you. I always said you took men and sex far too seriously, Zoe. Time to lighten up and enjoy yourself for a bit. Far from being foolish, I think you've chosen just the right type of man to have a fling with. He's drop-dead gorgeous to look at and he knows all the right moves. Best of all, you have no illusions about him."

"Yes, that's true. It's just that..." She sighed. "Oh, I don't know... Ever since I met Aiden, I haven't been myself. In a way it's good, but in another, it worries me."

"I think you're addicted to worry sometimes.

Look, you've already decided to have this fling. Then do so, without qualms, without doubts. And stop worrying. For pity's sake, you deserve some pleasure after Drake.''

''I do, don't I?''

''Yes.''

''Wish me luck.''

''What's luck got to do with it?''

Zoe thought about that. ''Nothing. Which reminds me, I'll have to buy some condoms on my way up there. It wouldn't be in keeping with the new me to rely on the man to provide protection. I should have my own.''

''I bought a new box the other day, and it doesn't even look like I'll be opening it. Do you want it?''

''How many?''

''Half a dozen.''

''Nah. Not enough. I'll buy some on the way.''

''Not enough? Now I *am* impressed. You won't be able to walk by the end of the week. Is he built?''

''You have to see it to believe it!''

Mel groaned. ''Lucky you. I'd like to see Jonathon's. I've felt it, mind you, pressed up against me, and it feels formidable.''

''You could get him into the sack if you put your mind to it, Mel.''

''Yeah, I know. But maybe I don't want to. Maybe underneath, I like it when he says he wants to wait awhile. Maybe I like hearing him say how much he loves me all the time.''

Mel's words stabbed at Zoe's heart, but she valiantly ignored the pain. She was sure love was wonderful if it was true, but she could do without the false hope of it.

''I must get going,'' Zoe said, putting her mug down. ''It's gone noon. Now I won't promise to call. If anyone wants to desperately get in touch with me, give them my cell phone number. I won't leave it on, but I'll check my message bank every day.''

''Aren't you going to eat something before you go?''

''No. I don't feel hungry.'' Not for food, anyway.

''Wow, that's a first!''

''I might stop off and have something on the way.''

She didn't. But she did drive past the turnoff to Hideaway Beach and went on into Nelson Bay where she bought packets of condoms at three different shops, too embarrassed to buy them all at one. So much for her pussy power!

And then she sat over a sandwich and cappuccino for another hour, trying to get her head around what she was about to do.

It was all very well for Mel to tell her not to worry. Mel had been having sex since puberty. And all kinds of sex, from the stories she told. She was an old hand at ''just sex'' relationships, whereas Zoe was a novice. What if she couldn't help getting emotionally involved with Aiden? What if she *did* fall in love with him?

What if, what if, a darkly impatient voice piped up inside her head. *Your whole life could go by if you keep sitting here, saying what if? Stop being so wishy-washy. Get up and get your butt over to his place. And when you get there, don't go all mushy and over the moon. Be strong. Be assertive. Be the woman you want to be.*

The stern self-lecture worked, propelling her to her feet and out to where she'd parked her car. She didn't waiver in her resolve during the relatively short drive back to Hideaway Beach, but when she arrived at Aiden's house and saw his yellow truck parked in the carport, fireworks started exploding in her stomach.

Shaking her head, she edged slowly down the steep driveway and slid into the space next to Aiden's van, swallowing as she turned off the ignition.

She didn't get out straight away. She sat for a while and tried to calm her madly racing heartbeat, not sure if she was afraid or excited. Possibly a bit of both.

She was still sitting there when Aiden materialized in front of the car and just stood there, glaring at her through the windshield. He was wearing those raggedy old denim board shorts and nothing else. His hair was sticking up all over the place, indicating a recent swim, and his chin was beginning to sprout some blond stubble. He looked pretty much as he had when she'd first met him. Roughly handsome and sinfully sexy.

Seeing him like that again made Zoe go all squishy inside.

Be strong, be assertive, she reminded herself as she climbed out from behind the wheel and looked him up and down.

''Been for a swim already, have you?''

''You're late,'' he snapped.

''Am I?'' She turned and swung the car door shut before facing him again. ''I didn't realize I had to be here at a certain time. Besides, I had things to do. I had to pack. And to change.''

''So I see. You do realize you're wearing far too many clothes,'' he growled.

''I didn't think it would be this hot up here.''

''It's even hotter inside.''

''I'll be fine after I have a cool shower.''

''I'll show you the way.''

''I'll just get my things.''

''Leave them,'' he said sharply, and she glared at him.

''Leave them,'' he repeated more quietly. A request this time, not a command.

Zoe shrugged, struggling now to remain strong and independent. Suddenly, she wanted to run to him, surrender to him, be a slave to him.

She could not understand it. After all she'd vowed!

He reached out his hand and she found herself placing hers in it, letting him draw her with him up onto the front verandah then into the house.

It was hot inside, as he'd said it would be. But not as hot as *she* was inside. He led her down the hallway and into the bathroom, closing the door behind them, closing the world out. With a darkly frustrated groan, he took her face captive in his hands and kissed her harshly, hungrily.

There was no stopping him then. He was like some starving beast who'd unexpectedly come across food. Zoe felt like she was being eaten alive, but, oh, how she loved it. Loved the feel of his mouth devouring hers. Loved his hands ripping off her clothes, then his own. Suddenly, there were no doubts or qualms. This was why she'd come. This was what she wanted.

Barely sixty seconds after his lips had first crashed down onto hers, Aiden was pulling her, panting and naked, into the shower.

The spray hit her breasts first. And then her face. Not cold. Hot. Hot as they were. She gasped and spun 'round in his arms, putting her back to the wetness and the heat. His hands encircled her throat, his thumbs tipping up her chin before rubbing roughly over her bruised mouth.

"Five minutes ago, I wanted to kill you," he muttered, his eyes never leaving hers. "Where have you been all this time?"

"I stopped off on the way to have something to eat," she confessed breathlessly. "And to buy some condoms."

He laughed. "Obviously not at Tom's store. I emptied his supply. The poor old guy thought I was going to an orgy. See?" And he pointed to the pile of plastic squares sitting on the shelf built into the shower wall. "I stashed some in every available nook and cranny in the house. I wanted them to be on hand, no matter where we were. The trouble was, while I was doing that, I started thinking of how I was going to do it to you in that particular place, or room. By the time I finished I had to go for a swim to cool down."

Her head spun with his words. "And how are you going to do it to me in here?" she choked out.

"That depends."

"On what?"

‘‘Have you ever made love in a shower before?’’ he murmured as he licked at her bottom lip.

‘‘No,’’ she admitted with a quiver.

‘‘How about anywhere other than a bed?’’

‘‘Only with you.’’

‘‘Oh, Zoe,’’ he groaned. ‘‘You do things to me which shouldn’t be allowed. Here. Feel this,’’ he said, and taking her hand, pressed it against his erection.

She not only felt it, she began caressing it. So velvety soft. Yet so hard. And all because of her.

Her hand curled ’round to grip him tightly before sliding seductively up and down. Up and down. He gasped and leaned back against the tiles, staring down at what she was doing as though he couldn’t believe it.

It was an empowering sight, and gradually, Zoe began to feel as she wanted to feel. Not like some submissive love slave. But a love goddess. No, a sex goddess. A wickedly seductive sex goddess.

So what if she hadn’t done a lot of things before! She knew about them. And she wanted to do them now. She wanted to do *all* of them.

He moaned shakily when she sank down onto her knees.

She glanced up at him through the shower spray which was now beating against his chest, the water running down his body, the rivulets parting to stream down on either side of his straining erection. He sucked in sharply when she grasped it firmly at the root, directing its straining length away from his stomach and into her mouth, her head dipping as she took him in inch by inch.

When she'd gone as far as she could go, she lifted her head slowly once more, sucking him tightly as she withdrew. He stiffened, trembled, groaned. She kept on doing it, her head rising and falling. When she stopped once to run her tongue around the tip, he jackknifed away from the tiles, gasping.

Her head lifted in a panic. "Did I hurt you?"

"Hardly," he muttered. "But if you do too much of that, I'll come."

"So?" She didn't care if he came, which was amazing. If Drake had suggested such a thing, she'd have been sick on the spot.

He stared down at her for several seconds, then sank back against the tiles, his eyes squeezing shut. "Heaven help me."

Zoe gathered that was the signal to go on. She did, her confidence soaring, her own pleasure immense. She'd heard of power trips but this was the ultimate. She could not get enough of the noises he made, or the feelings they evoked within her. The elation. The excitement. She learned to draw him in deeper and deeper, to suck him just long enough without tipping him over the edge. To stroke and fondle him with wickedly intimate hands at the same time.

"Zoe, stop," he pronounced suddenly, and snapped off the shower. "You have to stop."

She stopped, her eyes glazed as she glanced up. Hadn't he liked what she'd been doing?

He reached down and pulled her up onto unsteady feet, steam rising all around them. "You can do that another time. But not now. Not this first time. I just want you, Zoe. Nothing else. You, in my arms, and your eyes where I can see them.''

He reached for a condom and ripped it open with his teeth, his eyes never leaving hers. Their gazes remained locked while he protected them both, then pushed her legs apart. She swayed and had to brace herself against his chest.

''Keep looking at me,'' he ordered.

She did, her eyes growing round when she felt him rubbing the tip of his penis between her lips down there, grazing over her swollen clitoris with each stroke.

''Don't keep doing that,'' she gasped at last. ''I can't stand it. Just put it in. Please, Aiden…''

He put it in, his swift upward surge lifting her up onto her toes. His hands gripped her behind and he hoisted her up onto his hips, the position allowing him to slide home to the hilt, filling her totally.

It was better than she'd dreamed about.

Better.

Bigger.

''Oh,'' she panted, grabbing at his shoulders for support.

''Brace your feet against the wall behind me,'' he urged. ''I'll hold you in position. Bend then straighten your knees.''

''I…I can't.''

''Yes, you can. Squeeze me tight at the same time.''

She managed it, her mouth gaping open as sensation followed sensation. Oh, it felt so good. So unbelievably good.

His groan echoed her own sentiments. And her rapture.

''That's just incredible,'' he rasped. ''Keep doing it... Don't stop... Faster... Yes, that's the way... darlin'....''

His words excited her unbearably. They were wild and primitive, as their mating was wild and primitive.

Zoe came first, and then Aiden, their cries mingling, their bodies shuddering as their passion exploded from within.

It was some time before their spasms subsided, but they still clung to each other, Zoe sobbing with aftershock, and Aiden rubbing her back, trying to comfort her, his own thoughts confused.

Was she really upset? he began to worry when the weeping continued. If so, why?

It was what she wanted, wasn't it? It was why she'd come here, or so she insisted.

So why was she crying?

When her sobbing quietened to the odd hiccup, he carefully eased himself out of her and lowered her feet onto the floor. Her legs went to jelly and he had to hold her upright. ''Are you all right?'' he asked gently.

She looked up at him through soggy lashes. ''What a silly question,'' she choked out, then shivered.

''You're cold.'' He reached out to snap a large fluffy orange towel off the rack, wrapping it around her shoulders.

Her yawn startled her. ''I think I'm more tired than cold.''

''Want me to carry you to bed?''

She nodded, and he swept her up into his arms, the towel still around her.

She sighed an exhausted sigh and snuggled into him, her cheek resting against his chest, right over his heart. It fluttered, then filled with the most overwhelming emotion. Aiden's arms tightened around her and he knew, without a shadow of a doubt, that he loved this girl. Loved her as he had never loved before. Loved her passionately. Possessively, and rather painfully.

It hadn't been sexual frustration which had racked his insides by the time she'd arrived today. He'd been worrying his guts out that she might have had a car accident.

Now that he'd made love to her properly again, he could not bear to think of her ever being with another man. He wanted her to be his woman, forever. He wanted to live with her, have children with her, grow old with her. Hey, he even wanted to marry her.

And that was not something Aiden considered lightly.

Marriage, he'd always thought, was not for him.

There again, he hadn't met his true love at that stage.

He smiled at what his mother was going to say when he told her. Not that he intended to make such a confession just yet. He had things to do first...like get Zoe to fall in love with him in return.

Aiden carried her down the hallway toward his bedroom, his mind whirling with plans and possibilities. Could he get her to fall in love with him in a week?

Probably not.

Zoe wasn't in the mood for love.

But she was in the mood for sex. Oh, yes. She surely was that.

His stomach contracted as he thought of her going down on him in the shower. She'd been good, for a beginner. More than good. She'd been downright amazing.

Aiden glanced down at her lovely face as he angled her through the bedroom doorway. Her hair was plastered back from it but there was one stray curl stuck to her forehead. He smiled, thinking of that naughty version of the verse about the little girl with the curl in the middle of her forehead. When she was good she was very very good, but when she was bad, she was fucking fantastic!

Aiden understood that Zoe wanted to be bad for a while. Bad in her eyes, that is. Personally, he didn't believe that sex between consenting adults was ever bad, provided you didn't hurt anyone. And who were they hurting? No one.

But Zoe hadn't been brought up like him. She'd been raised with more old-fashioned ideas where it wasn't nice for girls to have sex without love.

Aiden didn't subscribe to that theory at all. Girls had just as much right to enjoy sex for sex's sake as guys did. To have fun for the moment, without always thinking of tomorrow.

So what if she wanted to be treated strictly as a sex object for a week? To try positions she'd never tried before. To explore her sexuality to the outer limits.

He could handle that, provided it was *him* she was

doing the exploring with. Aiden's smile turned wry. Amazing how, when you loved a woman, you weren't quite as liberal-minded about their sexual activities.

Holding her with one arm, he threw back the quilt, eased the towel away then lowered her nicely naked body into his nice big bed.

She immediately rolled over, curling her legs up into the fetal position. He stared at her deliciously curved bottom for a few seconds, before sighing and rather reluctantly covering her up.

''You'll keep,'' he muttered under his breath.

''Aiden,'' she mumbled.

He bent down and kissed the top of her head. ''What, darlin'?''

''Aren't you coming to bed with me?'' she asked dreamily.

''In a little while.''

''Oh...all right. 'Night.''

He didn't like to tell her it was still afternoon. '''Night. Sleep tight.''

She didn't hear him. She was already asleep.

17

ZOE half woke to the feel of someone sliding into bed with her. She automatically rolled over onto her left side, facing the wall, before her memory clicked in and her eyes snapped open into the darkened bedroom. Night had fallen, but there was some moonlight filtering through the open window.

"Aiden?" she choked out.

"Who else?" he said, his arms snaking 'round her waist and scooping her back against him. "All rested now?" he murmured, his head right behind hers, his lips nibbling at her shoulder.

"What...what time is it?"

"Around nine. Why? Does it matter?"

"No. I guess not."

She shivered when his mouth blew warm puffs in her right ear. When he dipped his tongue in and swirled it around, she stiffened, her legs shooting straight out, her behind discovering he was as naked as she was.

His hands started to travel over the front of her body, playing with her breasts, her stomach, then lower. Despite her own insistence that their time together would be focused on sex, her mind initially recoiled at being used in this way. Her body, however, seemed to like it, and in no time she was panting and wriggling her bottom against his erection.

''You're an impatient little thing, aren't you?'' he muttered. ''Just as well I wore one of my trusty condoms to bed.''

Zoe moaned softly when he eased into her from behind.

She wasn't surprised at the position, or the pleasure. He'd done it this way to her on the first night they spent together, and she'd loved it. They were like two spoons, curved around each other.

''You really like it this way, don't you?'' he murmured as he rocked gently into her, his hands caressing her nipples at the same time.

''Yes,'' she gasped.

It felt fantastic. *Too* fantastic. She was going to come and she didn't want to come. Not that soon. She wanted it to go on and on. She wanted...

He slid out of her and she cried out in dismay. His arms squeezed tightly around her, his own breathing ragged. ''Patience, my love. Talk to me for a while. It doesn't have to be anything deep and meaningful. I just need a breather and so do you. Try to relax.''

Relax! Was he insane? How could she relax when she was screaming inside and when he was still hugging her to him like this, his erection stabbing at her bottom?

''What books do you like to read?'' he asked.

''What? Oh...er...um...anything which doesn't bore me.''

''You must like thrillers, then.''

"Thrillers? Well...some of them. It depends on the author."

"Which author do you like most?"

"I can't think."

"Try."

"Um...Stephen King, I suppose."

"No kidding. I'm mad about Stephen King. I only discovered reading for pleasure this past year and he's the one I have to credit for doing it. My mom gave me *The Running Man* and I haven't had my nose out of one of his books ever since. Have you read *The Green Mile?*"

"Yes."

"It's great, isn't it?"

"Yes, but I liked *The Stand* even more."

"I haven't read that one."

"Oh, you should. It..."

Zoe was to wonder later how it came about that they started talking about Stephen King's books and she forgot all about sex. Until, that is, Aiden reminded her by lifting her right leg up onto his hip and slipping inside her once more.

"I think we might try something slightly different," he said, and rolled over onto his back. Naturally, she went with him, since his arms were wrapped tightly around her waist at the time. She ended up lying on top of him, her back stretched out along his front. He remained inside her, but not quite as deeply.

He let go of her waist and spread her arm and legs wide on the bed on either side of him. She looked and felt like a primitive virgin sacrifice stretched out on the altar of his naked body. No longer a virgin, however, in any sense of the word. She'd never felt so decadent. Or so turned on.

"Tell me what you're thinking?" he asked, his hands skimming up and down the length of her body, grazing over her rigid nipples.

"I...I can't..."

"Yes, you can. You can tell me anything."

"But I can't even *think!*"

He laughed then took her right hand in his and carried it down, down to that excruciatingly sensitive bud of swollen flesh which was at that moment wickedly exposed to the warm night air.

"Touch yourself there," he whispered, pressing her fingers against it.

Her mind once again recoiled but her body had a will of its own.

"Don't come," he advised softly. "Be gentle. Tease yourself. Work out what gives you pleasure without sending you over the edge."

Zoe could not believe she was doing this. Touching herself while he watched and instructed. But once she got over the initial stabs of embarrassment, it was an incredible turn-on. Soon, she was writhing on top of him, her behind clenching and unclenching. A climax was only seconds away.

When he abruptly grabbed her hips and lifted her right off him, she swore at him in mindless frustration.

"Tch, tch," he said, dumping her on the bed beside him and looming over her, his hands pinning her shoulders to the bed. "What would your father say if he heard you using words like that?"

''He'd probably agree with me if he knew what you were up to,'' she ground out. ''He thinks you're a great guy. Genuine and sincere. He doesn't know that you're a sexual sadist.''

He grinned down at her. ''Think of me more as your erotic educator rather than the Marquis de Sade. I'm teaching you to wait. It will be well worth it in the end. Trust me. I'm also giving poor old Percy here a short rest. He almost lost it again a second ago which will never do. Obviously, he's in sorry need of some serious practice. That six months' spell I inflicted on him hasn't done him any good at all. Hopefully, with a bit of patience and help, he'll be right back in tip-top form in no time.''

Zoe didn't think poor old Percy, who was pressing into her stomach at that precise moment, felt at all poor, or old. ''Do you seriously expect me to believe that before I came along you'd gone six months without sex?''

''Do you seriously expect me to believe you haven't gone down on a guy before me?'' he countered just as cynically.

She opened her mouth, then closed it again.

''Think about it, Zoe. Things aren't always what they appear to be. On top of that, why would I lie? What reason could I possibly have?''

She considered a few possibilities. To impress her somehow? To get under her guard? To make her think he wasn't anything like Drake who obviously couldn't go a week without his regular dose of slut?

None of those answers seemed to gel, which meant he hadn't lied to her. He'd been telling the truth about going six months without sex. Which led to another question. *Why?*

The concept that he might have been seriously hurt by that woman who took him to court was an explanation Zoe didn't want to think about. Because if she did, it meant she was starting to get involved. To care.

She couldn't do that to herself again. Not again. Not this soon, anyway.

"I have no idea," she said. "And I don't really want to know. I'm sorry I asked."

"Don't be," he returned just as nonchalantly. "It served a purpose. You've stopped swearing at me for not letting you come. So, are you hungry? For food, I mean."

Now that he mentioned it, she *was* hungry. It seemed her appetite had returned. And her desperate need for a climax had lessened somewhat.

"You mean you're not going to torture me again?"

"Not for a while."

Was she relieved, or disappointed?

"What have you got to eat?"

"Let's see now...I have a wide selection of frozen food in my freezer, and a trusty microwave to heat them in, but I also make a mean omelette. And I have some excellent white wine chilling in the fridge. I saw you drinking some Chardonnay the other night so I picked up a few good bottles on the way."

"You don't need to get me drunk, you know," she said ruefully. "I'm already a sure thing."

He grinned. "I know."

She couldn't help it. She grinned back. He really was delightfully wicked.

And delightfully wicked she could cope with. Delightfully wicked was far removed from anything deep and meaningful.

"An omelette sounds great. And the wine, too."

"Fantastic." He let her go and leaped out of the bed, turning to hold out his hand toward her.

She couldn't help but stare. "You're not going to walk around like *that,* are you?"

He glanced downward, then up again. "The condom bothers you?"

"No, but what's in it does," she said dryly. He was still fiercely erect.

Aiden shrugged. "At least this way I'm fully armed and ready if the heat of the moment overtakes us. But perhaps you're right. It might be dangerous cooking like this. I'll go to the bathroom and retrieve my shorts. But if you think you're going to put on those clothes *you* wore up here, Miss Pretend Prissy, then you can think again. Here..."

He marched over to the pine tallboy near the doorway and wrenched open the top drawer, pulling out a yellow T-shirt and tossing it to her. "Put that on. That's your uniform while you're here. No bra. And definitely no knickers. Just a T-shirt."

Zoe suppressed a laugh. "Yes, Sarge. Whatever you say, Sarge." Little did he know that wearing a man's T-shirt was overdressed compared to the scenario she'd fantasized over. But once she'd dragged it on, she could see that it was a surprisingly provocative garment. Her lack of underwear was patently obvious with her permanently hard nipples jutting through the thin material and her naked bottom was barely covered. She'd be a right sight if she stretched up or bent over.

"Wait for me," she said, and hurried down the hallway after Aiden.

ZOE found the next hour incredibly enjoyable. Aiden was an excellent cook and an entertaining companion. The wine was superb and so was the ambience of the front porch where they ate their omelettes and bread rolls, warm from the oven. They didn't sit at a table but perched on the porch steps, their plates balanced on their laps, their glasses of wine sitting beside them.

The night air was like warm velvet, the star-studded sky and half moon quite romantic. All was quiet at Hideaway Beach except for some distant music and the lap-lapping of the waves on the sand.

Zoe swallowed the last mouthful, then licked her fingers with a voluptuous sigh. "That was wonderful, Aiden. Thank you."

"My pleasure. Here, let me do that."

Before she could stop him, he took her right hand and sucked each finger in turn, a slow sensuous sucking which curled her stomach and brought her right back to where he'd had her an hour earlier.

"Do you provide this kind of personal after-dinner service for all your women?" she asked in an attempt to keep her cool.

He smiled wryly as he withdrew her little finger from his mouth. "Naughty, naughty," he said, shaking his head. "None of that getting-to-know-you stuff, you said. What I have or haven't done with previous women is on the no-no list of subjects for discussion.''

Zoe was a bit put out. She'd thought he *wanted* to get to know her. ''You asked me about my reading habits and I didn't object,'' she pointed out. ''And we've just spent the last hour chatting about food and wine.''

''Well, we do have to talk about something occasionally, don't we? And chatting about our tastes in books and food and wine is a far cry from revealing details of earlier relationships. Just sex, you said. And just sex you're going to get. So put your plate down, lover, and let's adjourn to the lounge room. I fancy a change of venue and some music. But bring your glass with you and I'll get the bottle. Your education is about to continue...''

18

AIDEN lay stretched out on top of his bed, his hands and feet secured to the four corners of his bed with various pieces of Zoe's underwear. She'd laughingly said they might as well be put to *some* use.

He still could not believe he'd agreed to this. Yet he had no one else to blame but himself. He'd created a monster!

''Having fun?'' Zoe asked as she sashayed back into the room, wearing his favorite orange T-shirt and looking very pleased with herself. And why not? She'd already had two orgasms to his none.

He regretted now having shown her how to stop him coming with one simple squeeze in just the right spot. He hadn't realized at the time how ruthlessly she would use that knowledge, once she had the chance.

Zoe's behavior this morning put paid to any egotistical idea she might be falling in love with him.

Over the last three days, he'd stupidly started hoping her feelings might be more than lust, because she was just so hot for him all the time. She never said no. He could have her anytime, anyplace, anywhere.

When she'd confided in bed this morning that she had a persistent fantasy about his tying her up, he'd been thrilled. Only a seriously besotted girl let a guy tie her up! So he'd been all for it. At that point she'd said she didn't really trust him enough for that, but she also fancied the idea of tying *him* up, if he didn't mind.

Naturally, at the time, he didn't mind one bit. He'd been so turned on he'd have agreed to being tied naked to a spit and roasted over hot coals!

And now here he was, spreadeagled and helpless. A lamb to her slaughter. The perfect victim for her increasingly insatiable appetite.

She wasn't in love with him at all, he finally had to accept. She'd just become sex mad!

He closed his eyes and groaned when she climbed onto the bed and straddled him once more.

"Poor Percy," she crooned as she pressed his rock-hard shaft painfully flat against his stomach. "And poor Aiden. You just have to learn to wait, don't you?" she said, smiling as she bent down to kiss him long and lasciviously, her tongue a worse temptation than the snake in the garden of Eden.

He moaned when she stopped.

"Beg for mercy," she murmured against his lips.

"Never," he bit back.

She smiled. "So be it."

She climbed off the bed and left the room.

Aiden would have screamed and shaken the bed if his pride had let him. But that was what she wanted. She wanted him to become frantic, and to beg.

Be blowed if he would ever do that!

She didn't come back for at least twenty minutes by which time things had thankfully subsided somewhat. But when Aiden saw she was carrying a tray of ice cubes, Percy snapped to attention once more.

"Don't," he croaked before he could stop himself.

"Don't what?" she asked in mock innocence. "You don't know what I'm going to do."

Yes, he did, because he'd done it to her yesterday. Used ice cubes on her nipples. And other places.

She smiled, popped an ice cube into her mouth and climbed up onto the bed.

Aiden gritted his teeth and tried not to cry out. But the sensations threatened to overwhelm him. Talk about fire and ice!

Fellatio on the rocks was a first for him and quite an experience. After the initial shock, the ice made his blood cool and his erection retreat, but that didn't last long. Eventually the cube melted and she didn't stop to get more. She kept on doing what she knew he liked best, taking him closer and closer to a climax. His hips began to lift from the bed and his mind and body strained toward the finishing line.

He couldn't believe it when she abandoned him again, right on the brink. When she got two more ice cubes out of the tray, it took every ounce of his control not to beg.

"Don't worry," she said with wildly glittering eyes. "This won't hurt a bit." And she rubbed them over his male nipples.

His body jerked, his mouth gasping open, his arms snapping his bonds tight as he fought to break free.

He swore. A lot.

She gave him a stunned look. "You don't like it?

But *I* did when you did it to me. I thought it was incredible.''

''I can't stand it,'' he bit out, terrified that if she kept on, he'd be doing worse than begging. He'd be embarrassing himself, totally.

''Well, you only had to say so,'' she said, looking unsure of herself for the first time that day. ''I wouldn't do anything I didn't think you were enjoying. Do you want me to untie you, too?''

Did he?

''No,'' he had to admit. He hadn't been this excited, or this hard, ever before. ''Not yet. But please, Zoe. Stop all that other stuff and make love to me. Properly.''

MAKE *love* to him?

Zoe was taken aback. He hadn't used that particular phrase all week. He'd called what they'd been doing everything else but.

A traitorous warmth curled through her stomach 'til she reminded herself they were still just words, especially in the mouths of men. Did any of them know what making love meant? Or what love meant? Did *she* anymore, for that matter?

She'd thought she loved Greg. She'd really thought she loved Drake. But both had been an illusion and neither had been able to make her feel what Aiden could make her feel. He only had to look at her and she wanted him. He only had to touch her and the craving would return.

It would be so easy to think of those feelings as love.

But they weren't. That was the hard lesson she'd learned this week. It was just sex. What they'd been doing for the last three days had been just sex. What she was about to do to him was still just sex.

But what the heck? If he wanted to call it making love then she wasn't about to object. He could call it whatever he darned well liked. She wasn't going to go all gooey over a silly phrase.

''My pleasure,'' she murmured, and moved to get one of the condoms which were always at the ready on the bedside table. She had it on him in seconds, having become an expert at the task. He liked her doing it. He said he found it a turn-on.

Not that he needed turning on at that moment. His erection was huge. At least he wanted her. That she *was* sure of.

''Take off the T-shirt,'' he said thickly when she straddled him once more. ''I want to see all of you.''

She shouldn't have done what he wanted. She should have smiled and told him that he was hardly in the position to give orders. This was *her* game. She was the one with the whip hand.

But there was something in his voice and in his eyes which she couldn't resist. So she crossed her arms and took the hem of the T-shirt and slowly lifted it up over her head before tossing it away. Staying up on her knees, she watched his eyes while she ran her hands over her breasts.

He groaned. ''God, don't do that. Not without me inside you. Put it in, Zoe. For pity's sake.''

For pity's sake?

She had no pity for him. But she still did what he wanted.

He sighed with pleasure and closed his eyes. Just in time, too. Because as she took him deep into her body, something happened to Zoe, something perturbing. A great wave of emotion flooded her chest, and tears pricked at her eyes.

That stupid phrase, she thought despairingly. That stupid, stupid phrase!

If only he hadn't said it. If only he'd used one of those other four-letter words they'd both bandied around all week. Why did he have to mention love?

Angrily, she began to move on top of him in the way he'd shown her, desperately trying to focus on nothing but the sex. Physically, it was even better than it had ever been. He was so big. But emotionally, she felt distraught and empty. Suddenly, she didn't want him tied up and she didn't want to be on top. She wanted to be beneath him, with their arms around each other and their mouths locked. She wanted tenderness, not kinkiness. She wanted his whole body, wrapped warmly and securely around her.

In short, she wanted Aiden to make love to *her* properly, not just have sex with her.

Zoe groaned her dismay at what this meant. She had fallen in love with the man. Against all common sense, and all her best resolves. It was irrational to love him, but it was no less real. Awfully painfully real.

''Zoe?'' he choked out, his eyes opening. ''Why have you stopped, darling?''

She wished he hadn't called her darling. It was like

a dagger into her heart because it was so patently false. But it gave her focus. And courage. And some return to common sense.

"Just giving poor old Percy a rest," she said matter-of-factly.

"He doesn't need a rest," Aiden groaned. "He needs you."

"Really. Well, come next week, he'll have to find someone else, won't he?"

He stared at her and she knew all of a sudden that he wouldn't let her go quite that easily. She'd been more than a good lay over the last few days. She'd been his very own love slave, ready and willing to accommodate him twenty-four hours a day.

Her silly female heart fluttered wildly before she took hold of it once more. At least he doesn't know you love him, she reminded herself. He knows nothing except what you tell him.

Be strong. Be firm. Be assertive. There'll never be a better moment to show him what you're made of, with him flat on his back and unable to move.

"Don't look so down in the mouth," she said blithely, and returned to her rising and falling rhythm. "A man like you won't take long to find a replacement."

"And what if I don't want a replacement?" he grated out.

"You can't always have what you want in life, Aiden," she said as she continued her ruthless rhythm. "I've certainly learned that. I'm surprised you haven't. Money doesn't buy everything, you know."

"I know that, but I... Oh..." He gasped, then grimaced.

Understandable. She'd begun squeezing him tightly with her insides. She had to do something to shut him up and change the subject.

"Do stop talking, lover," she advised dryly. "We both know that men can't do two things at once, unlike us clever little females." I can even do this and break my heart at the same time! "Close your eyes again and just let it go."

And let *me* go, she willed fiercely.

He closed his eyes and came with a rush.

Depressingly, so did she.

Zoe had never hated a climax more.

19

"I'M GOING surfing," Aiden said, and waited for Zoe to say something.

She was lying on her stomach on the bed, her arms curved up under the pillow, her face turned away from him. She'd flopped down there after she'd untied him, saying she was exhausted and needed a nap.

"Fine," she said without moving an inch. "Have fun."

He glowered down at her naked back, then whirled and marched out, wondering what in heaven's name he'd ever seen in her.

Okay, so she'd been a real honey when he'd first met her, but she wasn't anymore. She'd become a tough, cynical, sex-driven bitch!

"You can't have everything in life you want," he sneered as he stomped out onto the front porch. "No kidding!"

A strong gust of wind startled Aiden out of his mutterings. It was another hot day, but by the look of the darkening sky and the storm clouds gathering on the horizon, a southerly change was on the way.

Hideaway Beach was not a good surf in these conditions. The waves would get bigger, but dumping.

And the tide would become stronger and more dangerous.

But he was going surfing, come hell or high water. He'd drive over to Fisherman's Beach which was much more open. The waves there would still be big, but rolling, and less risky.

No, he'd *walk* over to Fisherman's Beach. It was a long walk, but he didn't care. He needed a couple of hours away from Zoe.

Leaving his lighter board leaning against the verandah, he collected a trusty old favorite from the roof of his van, tucked it under his arm and set off across the sand. He briefly thought of going back and telling Zoe where he was going, but that seemed so pathetic. And needy.

She'd still be there when he got back. After all, she hadn't had her daily quota of orgasms!

And if she wasn't?

Aiden decided testily that might be for the best.

ZOE wept quietly into the pillow for a long time after Aiden left.

How could she have been so stupid as to fall in love with him? Mel would be so disappointed in her, but not as disappointed as she was with herself.

Thinking of Mel, however, reminded Zoe that she hadn't checked the message bank on her cell phone since she arrived. Understandable, considering her mind had been elsewhere. She hoped no one had been trying to get into contact with her urgently.

Zoe sighed and sat up, swinging her feet over the

side of the bed. Now where was that T-shirt? And where was her handbag?

She finally found it hanging on a chair in the kitchen.

Zoe winced as she ran through the messages. Betty had tried to ring her yesterday. Fran, too. Both had left a message for her to ring them back. But Fran had added as soon as possible.

Which one first?

Zoe dialed her work number.

''Phillips & Cox,'' June answered.

''Fran Phillips, please,'' Zoe said, using a brisk, business-like voice and hoping June didn't recognize her. The last thing she wanted to do was answer the office gossip's questions.

Thankfully, she was put straight through to Fran.

''It's Zoe, Fran. I got your message to call.''

''Zoe. I'm so glad you rang back. Sorry to bother you when you're on holidays.''

''What's up? Something to do with work?''

''No. Not at all. But, this is harder than I thought it would be. No one likes to be the bearer of bad tidings but I thought you should know exactly what's been going on behind your back.''

''Ah,'' Zoe said, the penny dropping. ''You've seen Drake and Tracy together. She's blond. Big boobs. Mouth to match.''

''You know about her?'' Fran sounded shocked.

''I caught Drake with her in flagrante delicto last Saturday night at his party. I dumped him then and there, so don't worry, Fran. I know exactly what's been going on behind my back. I dare say it's been going on for quite some time.''

''I *knew* there was something more to your wanting time off than just your father breaking his ankle. I just couldn't work out what 'til I saw that disgusting piece of work with Drake at the pool together. She was all over him like a rash. And he was so drunk. I was appalled and I told him so. I can't tell you the language he used back. And in full hearing of lots of people. Goodness knows what's got into him. He'll ruin himself both socially and professionally if he keeps on behaving like that.''

''Good,'' Zoe pronounced. But it wasn't good. It was rather sad, really. Zoe had an awful feeling Drake had loved her, in his own peculiar way. But he'd been addicted to a certain type of sex, the kind he didn't think he could get from her.

''Are you sure you're all right?'' Fran asked.

''I'm fine,'' Zoe lied.

''But you're not still down at your father's farm, are you?''

''N...no,'' she said carefully. ''Why?''

''This is awkward, too. Look, I'll just come right out and say it. The thing is, Zoe, I was so shocked by what happened with Drake that I couldn't help talking about it. Anyway, I was telling Nigel and saying how upset you must be, and this weird little smile came over his face. When I asked what was going on, he said not to worry about you too much, that you'd met someone a lot better than Drake and if he knew anything about life and love, you'd be coming back to work next week all rosy-cheeked and dewy-eyed. When I pressed him for the name of this white knight he said it was Aiden Mitchell, at which point I nearly had a hernia.''

``You don't think Aiden's a white knight?'' Zoe said ruefully.

``So, it's true! You're having a *thing* with Aiden Mitchell!''

``A fling, Fran. Not a thing. It's nothing serious.'' Except that her heart was breaking.

``Are you sure? Nigel seemed to think Aiden sounded pretty serious about *you.*''

Zoe's heart leaped. But only for a second. ``Nigel's a romantic.''

``And you're not?''

``Not anymore.''

``Oh. What a shame.''

Zoe was taken aback. ``What do you mean what a shame? I thought you thought I was a fool for being a romantic.''

Fran sighed. ``I guess I did, when it came to Drake. But Aiden Mitchell! Now he's worth being a bit romantic over. He's one seriously sexy guy. And not quite as callous as the newspapers painted him last year.''

``Not *quite?*'' Zoe queried, surprised that Fran would have anything good to say about him at all. ``What do you mean by that?''

``Look, I have to admit I don't know Aiden all that well. He was Nigel's client. But I recognize a right royal bitch when I meet one and that female who sued him tried to hire me first as her lawyer and I wouldn't touch her with a bargepole. She was an incredibly nasty piece of work. A clever liar, though. And Aiden, unfortunately, has this perversely honest streak. He refused to lie on the stand and that did him in, because when questioned, he admitted to sleeping with her. Then he foolishly added it had only been the once. No one in that courtroom believed him, other than Nigel.''

''Nigel believed he was telling the truth?''

''Yes, he did. And Nigel is a darned good judge of character, except when the guy concerned is gorgeous *and* gay. Which Aiden isn't.''

''No, he certainly isn't,'' Zoe agreed.

''I gathered that. I won't ask you what he's like in bed. I don't want to be jealous. Whatever, I'm glad to hear you're not devastated over Drake. But perhaps it's just as well this isn't serious between you and Aiden. It's a bit soon and you're only young, Zoe. You have all the time in the world. So have your fling. And have some fun. Now...you'll be back at work next Monday?''

''You can count on it,'' Zoe said firmly.

''I knew I could. 'Bye, Zoe. Take care.''

Zoe hung up, shaking her head and frowning. Hard to keep anything a secret in this world. She should have known Fran would find out, especially with Aiden having contacted Nigel in his pursuit of her.

Zoe didn't know what to make of Fran's revelations about Aiden's character. Considering her boss's cynicism about the male sex, Zoe had to take what she'd said at face value. Aiden must have been the injured party in that court case, which certainly would explain why he'd been reluctant to tell her the truth about himself when they'd first met.

Zoe's stomach churned at the thought that maybe Aiden was serious about her. He'd said he was, of course. In the beginning. But serious about what? Getting her into bed again?

Once he'd secured her promise to go away with him and she'd insisted on a strictly sexual affair, he'd quickly dropped all that I-want-a-real-relationship rubbish. Not once, over the last few days, had he tried to change the status quo. In fact, every time *she'd* asked him a personal question, he'd been quick to fob her off and get back to just sex.

Okay, so perhaps he wasn't the liar Drake had been. Maybe he did have some feelings for her other than sexual. He still wasn't a marrying kind of guy. Being his girlfriend was not going to be a permanent position.

No. She wasn't about to give Nigel's view of Aiden's so-called seriousness too much credence.

Neither did she want to get maudlin over the fact she'd fallen in love with the wrong man. Again.

She'd known what she was getting herself into here. She'd gone into it with her eyes well and truly open. Zoe had no one to blame but herself.

She rang Betty next.

Betty answered on the second ring.

"Betty, it's Zoe. I'm sorry I haven't called back sooner. I had my cell phone turned off and I've only just looked at my messages. What's up? Dad okay?"

"Is your dad okay, she says," Betty replied with a

happy lilt in her voice. "I'll say he is. You're never going to believe this."

"He's sold the farm?"

"What? Oh, yes, he's going to do that, too. But that'll take time. That's not why I've rung."

"So what else has Dad done?" As if she didn't know. He must have told Betty he loved her.

"Well, on Monday he made me take him into Moss Vale, crutches and all, and have his hair cut. And then he dragged me into the trendiest menswear shop in town and asked me to choose some new clothes for him. And then...oh, you're not going to believe this! *Then,* over lunch, he asked me to marry him."

"What?" Zoe was shocked. She'd thought he was going to wait awhile before he proposed. "So what did *you* say?"

"I said yes, of course. I've been in love with your dad for ages."

"You *have?*"

"There's no need to sound so surprised, missy. Your dad's a good-looking man for his age. You could have knocked me over with a feather when he said he'd been in love with *me* for ages."

"Now, there's no need for *you* to sound so surprised, Betty. You're a *very* good-looking woman. For any age."

"Oh, go on with you. I'm too tall, and too skinny and I have the most awful-colored hair."

"I'll have you know that my dad thinks you're so beautiful and so special that he didn't *dare* ask you to marry him before. He was sure you'd say no."

"He said that?"

"He did, indeed."

"Oh..." For the first time in her life, Zoe reckoned, Betty was speechless. But now Zoe knew the truth over why Betty had never married. Because of low physical self-esteem. All the time she'd been helping Zoe to look better, Betty had probably believed her own looks were a lost cause.

"That is the best news I've had in simply ages," Zoe said. "I'm so happy for you both. Tell Dad I'm proud of him."

"Tell him yourself. *Bill?*" she called out. "Bill, it's Zoe on the phone. She wants to talk to you."

"Zoe."

"Hi there, Dad."

"I did it."

"You certainly did. I'm very proud of you."

"I'm pretty proud of myself. I was going to wait 'til I lost some weight but I decided not to. Life's too short. But I've started watching my diet already, and I'll get right into some proper exercise once I get this plaster off my ankle. Meanwhile, I'm selling the farm and organizing a wedding."

"And when do you think the wedding will be?"

"As soon as we can arrange it. Betty's never been married and I thought she'd like a nice church wedding. What do you think?"

"I think that's sweet." Suddenly, tears filled Zoe's eyes.

There'd be no nice church wedding for her with the man she loved. No wedding of any kind.

"You'll tell Aiden?" her father said.

"Tell who what?" Her thoughts had left her distracted.

"Did I get it wrong? I thought you'd gone away for a few days with Aiden. He'd said you were."

Any tears quickly dried up, replaced by annoyance. "Did he now? Well, he had no right to do that."

"Why not? Anyone could see you're crazy about each other. I don't know why you thought you had to pretend you weren't. I'm no fool, Zoe. I know you and Aiden are more than just good friends. I just want you to know that I heartily approve."

"You approve of my sleeping with Aiden?" Zoe blurted out, astonished. He certainly hadn't approved of her sharing her room with Drake at Christmas.

"No. Of your loving him. He's the real McCoy. So don't let this one get away."

"And what if he wants to get away?"

Her dad chuckled. "Aiden? Want to get away from you? Why would he want to do that? He loves you!"

Zoe's heartbeat bolted. "Did he say that to you?"

"Of course not. I could just tell."

Her heart skittered to a halt, her sigh weary. What a fool she was to get her hopes up like that. Her father had about as much insight into matters of the heart as one of his cows. He'd practically been living with Betty all these years and hadn't gleaned *her* true feelings.

"Whatever you say, Dad."

"You don't believe me!" He sounded truly shocked.

"Let's just say I'll wait for the proposal of marriage."

"Proposal of marriage? He's not going to propose marriage! He's only just met you."

"I thought you said he loved me."

"Men don't propose marriage that quickly. Or that rashly. For one thing, they're afraid of being rejected. If you haven't told him you love him yet, he'll be worried you might not."

"I don't."

"Oh, yes, you do, daughter."

Zoe sighed again. "All right, I do. But I don't want to."

"Why not?"

"Because even if he does love me—and I don't think he does—he's on record as saying he's not a marrying man."

"He hadn't met you at that stage."

Zoe gave up. "Can we just leave this argument for now, Dad?"

"Promise me you'll tell him you love him."

"I can't do that."

"You mean you won't."

"All right, I won't."

"You made me tell Betty I loved her, and you were right. You said life was too short not to, and you were right again. Now take some of your own advice and tell him you love him. Just because one man hurt you, doesn't mean the next one will. I wasted over ten years of my life, thinking no woman would want me because I couldn't make your mother happy."

"Oh, Dad. Mom wasn't *that* unhappy."

"Yes, she was. But I see now we were just mismatched. It wasn't all my fault."

Zoe nodded. He was right. Her mom was not the sort of woman to cope with the lonely life as a farmer's wife. She was not strong enough, or independent enough. Her only outside interest had been her garden, and it hadn't been enough.

"Give Aiden a fair go," her father said. "Don't let past experiences blind you to the present. Promise me that, at least."

"All right," she agreed. "I promise. And, Dad..."

"Yes?"

"I've enjoyed talking to you. Now you take care of yourself and give my love to Betty."

She hung up, frowning over the promise her father had extracted from her. Perhaps she *had* been letting the past blind her to the present. Perhaps she hadn't *really* given Aiden a fair go.

Okay, so she might get hurt again if she took a chance and told him she loved him. But wasn't it worth the risk of further pain, even if there was the slightest possibility Aiden might truly care about her?

There was going to be heartache for her, anyway.

A rumble of thunder interrupted her thoughts. Frowning, Zoe hurried out onto the porch and was shocked that the weather could have changed so radically without her having noticed. Ominous-looking gray clouds covered the sky, blocking out the sun. A brisk wind was whipping up the ocean into high foam-topped waves which curled over and crashed down angrily onto the beach.

Scanning the water, Zoe couldn't see Aiden. She knew the spot he favored when he went board riding but he wasn't there. No one was there. No one was on the beach at all.

It started to rain, large pelting drops which would soak anyone in seconds.

Zoe walked down the end of the covered porch and peered 'round the side of the house to where her car and Aiden's truck were parked side by side. The yellow truck was still there, so Aiden hadn't driven off anywhere else. Which meant he must have gone surfing here.

It was then that she saw his surfboard, still leaning up against the post beside the front steps.

Zoe's stomach contracted into a tight knot of instant fear. Aiden must have gone body surfing, not board riding.

Oh, dear heaven...

Zoe's hands gripped the red porch railing with white-knuckled intensity, her now-frantic gaze searching the ocean once more. She still couldn't see anyone swimming, or body surfing. Not a single bobbing head anywhere.

Suddenly, the waves didn't just look large but lethal as well. Zoe remembered that treacherous tide which had carried her toward the rocks that night. Her eyes swung over toward those rocks and she was amazed to see a couple of fishermen standing on them, still fishing. They had to be insane, she decided. But maybe they could tell her if they'd seen Aiden.

Running back inside, she dragged on some shorts then raced back through the front door, hurtling down the front steps and launching herself across the sand, unmindful of the rain. She was quick across the sand but slow once she came to the rocks, where she had to pick her way carefully over their slippery surfaces toward where the two fishermen were recklessly standing with their rods.

"Hey, there!" she shouted when she didn't dare get any closer. As it was, every third wave washed over her lower legs, threatening her balance. "Have you seen anyone swimming in the surf this afternoon?"

"What?" one of them called back, whilst the other didn't even turn his head her way. He probably hadn't heard her with the wind and the rain and the waves.

She cupped her mouth with her hands and repeated her question. The fisherman shook his head and Zoe's heart sank. She doubted they would have noticed, anyway. Their focus was all on what they were doing.

For the next half an hour she walked up and down along the water's edge, getting soaked to the bone, but unable to go back to the house. If there'd been anyone else to ask for help, she would have, but Hideaway Beach was deserted. There wasn't a single vehicle in the visitors' car lot. Finally, in desperation, she went along and knocked on all the other doors of the weekenders, hoping that Aiden might have gone visiting.

But no one answered. They were weekenders, after all. And it was only a Thursday.

Zoe tried to cling to the hope that Aiden might have gone for a walk, but if that was so, surely he'd have come home once it started to rain. And it had been raining steadily for ages. The persistent thought that something dreadful had happened to him in the surf would not go away, bringing with it a sick churning to her stomach and an even sicker churning in her heart.

What if she never had the chance to tell him she loved him? What if it was all over between them in the most terrible and final way?

She couldn't bear it.

Despairingly, she returned to the house and in desperation picked up her phone. But who to call? If something disastrous had happened to Aiden in the surf it was already too late. She decided to call the triple-O emergency number, anyway, and was punching out the numbers when she heard the sound of a vehicle coming down the driveway. Dropping the phone, she dashed out onto the porch and raced 'round the side of the house.

A battered truck crunched to a halt behind the carport and Aiden jumped out of the passenger seat.

"Thanks for the ride, buddy," he called out as he retrieved a surfboard from the back.

"No sweat," the driver returned. "See you, Aiden." And he reversed up the driveway.

"What happened to you?" Aiden asked when he spotted Zoe standing there, soaked to her skin. "Go for a swim with your clothes on, did you?"

Zoe just stared at him, her emotions utterly mangled. She didn't know whether she wanted to kill him, or kiss him.

"No, you inconsiderate pig!" she threw at him. "I've been looking for your body!"

And she promptly burst into tears.

20

SHOCK held Aiden stock-still for a few moments, 'til suddenly, he saw the truth behind Zoe's tears.

She'd been worried sick about him. She thought she'd lost him. She truly cared about him.

He needed no other encouragement.

Dropping his board, he covered the distance between them in two strides and gathered her into his arms.

"You're right, I am inconsiderate. I walked over to Fisherman's Beach. I should have told you where I'd gone. I was angry with you because I didn't think you cared about me. I thought all you wanted from me was sex. But you do care, don't you, darling? Tell me I'm not wrong about that. Tell me you care."

He tipped up her chin so that he could see her eyes.

They were so beautiful, her eyes. And so expressive. He could see the fear in their glistening depths. But he could also see the love.

Or what he hoped was love.

"Don't be afraid to admit it," he said gently. "I won't hurt you like Drake hurt you. I love you, Zoe. With all my heart. I've never said that to any other girl in my life. I know you think I'm some kind of cheat with women because of that court case last year, but I'm not. I was the victim there, not her.''

"Tell me what really happened,'' Zoe asked.

"I met Marci at a party and we got talking. When she said she'd lost her job that week and had nowhere to live, I stupidly offered her the use of one of my spare rooms for a while. I didn't think anything of it, as I was hardly ever there. Admittedly, I began to feel she was overstaying her welcome after a few weeks went by and she didn't leave. But she always had some excuse why she couldn't move out and I had no real reason to throw her out. It wasn't as though I had a steady girlfriend at the time who was objecting. Then one night, when I came home after being away all week on business, she obviously set out to seduce me. And she succeeded. The next morning, when I explained to her that the night before was a mistake, she showed her true colors and said it was a mistake all right. Mine. She got herself a lawyer who made Attila the Hun look sweet and the rest is history. She was never my girlfriend, Zoe. And I never promised to marry her. My only crime was being a mug, for want of a better word.''

Zoe's eyes searched his face, obviously wanting to believe him, but still hesitant.

"I swear to you that that's the truth. On my mother's life,'' he added solemnly. "And if you ever get to know me as well I would like, you'll know I would not say that lightly. Because I simply adore my mother.''

Zoe's defenses melted away at this declaration.

"Tell me you love me," he persisted. "Right now. Tell me."

"I love you," she choked out.

The blinding joy which spread across his handsome face soothed any lingering doubts Zoe was still harboring about the sincerity of Aiden's feelings.

"About time, too," he said thickly, and held her close, cradling her head against his chest.

"I tried not to," she confessed. "I tried to keep things to just sex. I told myself I didn't want to get to know you at all, except in the biblical sense. But in my heart of hearts, I always wanted more from you than just sex. I thought I was being sensible and strong in keeping our relationship to a brief affair, when really, I was just being a coward."

He held her away from him, his eyes soft and sympathetic. "You? A coward? Oh, no, Zoe. You're no coward. You're very brave, and I love that in you. You have character and spirit and standards."

"How can you say that? I've been wicked this week. You know I've been wicked."

"Not at all. How can anything we do together be wicked when we love each other so much?"

"Oh, Aiden, I do so love you. What I felt for Drake wasn't real love. I can see that now. As for Greg…"

Zoe bit her bottom lip, but it was too late. She'd already blurted out Greg's name.

"Greg?"

Zoe saw the speculation in Aiden's eyes and decided she wanted no ghosts from the past to spoil what she might have with this man. "A creep I met when I first came to Sydney," she explained. "He was my immediate boss in the section of the insurance company I worked in. At the time I was on the plump side and very shy where the opposite sex was concerned. Apparently, he made a bet with his male colleagues that he could get me into bed within a fortnight. He did, by telling me lies about how attractive he found me and how much he desired me. I was a naive fool to believe him, but then, that's what I was at the time. A naive fool. The day after I lost my virginity to him, I overheard him at work laughingly relating how pathetic I was in bed. He told his buddies that they should pay him double the agreed wager because naked, my body was so gross.''

''Oh, Zoe...how awful for you. It makes me ashamed of my sex when I hear things like that. But not all men are as bad as Greg. Or Drake. Take me for instance,'' he added, suddenly smiling the cheekiest smile. ''I'm a prince.''

She laughed. ''You're an arrogant devil, that's what you are. You knew I'd fall in love with you if I came away with you.''

''I was hopeful.''

''Even when I said I only wanted sex?''

''That didn't worry me to begin with. I thought sex between us would be a very emotionally bonding experience. But I have to admit I started to worry this morning after I let you tie me to the bed.''

''I can imagine. I was a bad girl, wasn't I?''

''Mmm.''

''But as soon as you asked me to make love to you properly, I realized I didn't want that kind of sex anymore. I wanted to untie you and have you make love to me properly right then and there."

His beautiful blue eyes danced with a wry amusement. "Really. You gave a pretty good imitation of a girl only interested in her own pleasure."

"I didn't want you to know I loved you."

He laughed. "That's your story and you're going to stick to it, aren't you? Still, I see it's going to take me a while to convince you that I'm one of the good guys. I think, come tomorrow, I'm going to take you home to meet my mom. But first, I'm going to make love to the woman I love. Properly." And he swept her up into his arms.

"Tell me again that you love me," he said as he carried her back into the house.

"I love you, Aiden."

"I want to hear that a lot tonight."

"Yes, darling."

"And I want to hear *that* a lot, too!"

"I DIDN'T bring my hair-dryer with me," Zoe wailed as she inspected herself in the bathroom mirror the next morning. "And not much makeup, either. What will your mother think of me?"

Aiden smiled. "She'll think you're gorgeous. Just like I do."

"Really?"

Her insecurity over her appearance both irritated and touched him. "Your hair looks lovely as it is," he insisted, "and your skin has a wonderfully natural glow this morning."

Zoe had to admit that she *was* looking good. Being truly in love suited her. Or was it being truly loved?

"You don't have to be anything other than your beautiful self around me, Zoe. I do understand that clothes and grooming play an important part in the professional scene around Sydney, but let's leave it there, shall we?"

"I just want to make a good impression on your mom."

Aiden smiled and drew her to him. "You've already made a good impression by falling in love with me. You should have heard her on the phone last night. She was ecstatic. But there's no need to doll yourself up for my mom. She's not into that kind of thing."

"I'm still not going to wear shorts," Zoe told Aiden firmly. "I want to wear my lemon slacks and white shirt."

He pulled a face. "If you must."

"I must." She reached up on tiptoe and kissed him lightly on the lips. "I'll tie the shirt above my waist and I won't wear a bra," she whispered.

He grinned. "That's my girl."

And wasn't that the truth. She was Aiden's girl. For better or worse. For richer or poorer. But would it ever be 'til death do them part?

Hopefully. Zoe knew her dad was right when he said that men didn't propose marriage this quickly. But she felt confident Aiden was already committed to a real and lasting relationship between them. They'd talked a lot last night in between the tenderest of lovemakings, and Zoe had woken this morning feeling happy and optimistic.

There were no guarantees in life, of course. There were no guarantees in anything. But she wasn't going to spoil what she could have with him by indulging in negative thoughts. For once, she was going to enjoy each day as it came and not worry too much, as Mel had advised.

"Just give me another fifteen minutes," Zoe told Aiden, "and I'll be ready to leave."

"I'm going to hold you to that," he said. And did.

The drive north was pleasant, with the southerly change the day before bringing milder fall weather. Just as well, Zoe thought, since they were driving in Aiden's yellow truck and it didn't have air-conditioning. She didn't want to arrive at his mother's place with limp hair and perspiration stains all over her shirt.

Zoe and Aiden chatted companionably the whole way, and it wasn't till Aiden took the turn-off to Shelley Bay, that she began feeling nervous.

"I hope your mom really likes me," she couldn't help saying.

"Don't worry. She will."

Shelley Bay turned out to be a delightful little seaside spot which had no high-rise buildings to mar its semi-tropical beauty. The tall Norfolk pines which lined the white-sanded beachfront made it look like a hundred other coastal towns which dotted the Australian coastline.

"Never changes, Shelley Bay," Aiden remarked happily as he drove down the main street then took a road which wound its way into the hills behind the town. "Which is exactly the way I like it."

"Give it another ten years," Zoe warned, glancing at the magnificent view in the side mirror. "I'll bet some big developer will move in and build a huge resort up on this very hill, and then you'll see some changes."

"I doubt it. I happen to own this hill and I ain't selling."

Zoe was astonished. "You're that rich, Aiden?"

"Filthy rich, actually. But you don't have to worry, darlin'. I won't go buying you all sorts of expensive gifts or taking you to five-star restaurants or doing any of those wickedly corrupting things you once told me not to. But it's going to be very difficult when it comes to birthdays and Christmas if I can't even buy you flowers and perfume."

"Aiden Mitchell, stop teasing me. You know that was before."

He grinned. "Before what?"

"Before I believed you loved me."

"You mean I can spoil and corrupt you with my money now?"

She laughed. "I think you've already corrupted me. But heck yes, spoil me all you like."

"Great. Oops. Almost missed mom's place. Too much talking."

Aiden braked sharply and zapped the yellow truck up a steep and rather rocky driveway, which then flattened out and swung 'round in a circle in front of one of those delightful old wooden houses called Queenslanders. Given this one belonged to Aiden's mother,

Zoe should not have been surprised that it was painted a bright yellow, with white latticework and a deep terra-cotta roof.

Not that the color scheme didn't brilliantly suit its leafy-green setting. Huge gum trees on either side cast shade onto the roof whilst large tree palms and various exotic-looking ferns flanked the white-painted steps which led up onto the wide cool-looking porch.

Zoe was admiring it all when a woman emerged from the house and started walking down those steps, a woman who took Zoe's breath away.

She was tall and slender, with straight honey-blond hair which fell down to her waist. She was wearing an ankle-length, sarong-style skirt in turquoise silk, topped with a vivid scarlet singlet. Her feet were bare and her toenails were painted scarlet. As she drew closer Zoe saw she wore no makeup on her honey-colored skin. But she certainly wore jewelry.

Long multicolored hoops swung from her lobes. She had a gold stud in her right nostril and a snakelike silver bangle wrapped high around her left arm.

She looked exotic and sexy and not like anyone's mother Zoe had ever known.

"Oh, my, Aiden," Zoe gasped. "She's so beautiful."

"Who, Mom?" He seemed startled by the compliment. Then thoughtful. "Yeah, you're right. She is. But her soul is even more beautiful. Come on, come and meet her."

Kristy Mitchell's lovely face was even lovelier when she smiled. And she smiled at her son as he whisked her off her feet and whirled her 'round in greeting, kissing and hugging her at the same time.

Zoe watched, in a type of awe. Clearly, this was how this beautiful-looking woman had brought him up, with a lot of physical expressions of love. No wonder he was such a warm generous person and a simply wonderful lover.

"Aiden, put me down," his mom ordered at long last. "I'm very pleased to see you, too, darling, but don't you think it's time you introduced me to Zoe? That is why you've come, isn't it? So that I can see this very special girl who's revived your spirit and restored your soul."

Zoe's eyes widened at these amazingly flattering words. Was that what he'd told his mom she'd done for him?

She stared at Aiden who shrugged and smiled a little sheepishly at her.

"Trust my mom to embarrass me. But yes," he confirmed. "You did all that. And more." He took her hand and drew her to his side. "So what do you think of my Zoe, Mom? Isn't she lovely?"

Zoe colored a little as those beautiful blue eyes—so like her son's—gave her a long assessing look.

"I think," Aiden's mother said slowly, "that if she is that—*your* Zoe—then don't play games with her, son. Tell her what you told me last night. Tell her now."

Aiden groaned. He should have anticipated this. His mother would not let him make the same mistake she believed his father had once made.

"Aiden?" Zoe asked worriedly. "What does your mom mean? What is it you have to tell me?"

He closed his eyes and suddenly he felt as he'd felt once when he was out on his board and he saw this huge wave coming and he thought, I'm gone. He'd no option then but to gather all his courage and ride that rogue wave, because not to could have been the kiss of death to him as a professional surfer. He might have lost his nerve.

The situation was pretty much the same. He had to go for it. Had to. Because if he didn't, all might be lost. And losing Zoe would be a lot worse than losing his nerve.

He opened his eyes and looked straight at her. "I told my mother I was going to ask you to marry me one day in the near future. She seems to think that that one day should be today. And you know what? She's right. You are my one true love, Zoe. Why wait? Will you marry me?"

Zoe was overwhelmed. His one true love. He'd called her his one true love! On top of that, he'd proposed marriage!

"You don't have to give him an answer straight away," Aiden's mom said gently. "I just wanted him to be straight with you. After all you've been through with that other fellow, I thought you needed to hear up front just how much my boy loves you."

Aiden rolled his eyes. "Mom, will you shut up? And she *does* have to answer straight away. If I've had the guts to ask her, then she has to have the guts to answer me. So what's it to be, Zoe?"

Zoe wondered dazedly what all her friends and

family would say if they were standing here at this moment. Fran. Mel. Betty. Her dad.

Especially her dad.

What would he say to her?

A small smile played around Zoe's lips as she realized exactly what her dad would say.

Go for it, girl. Go for it.

And the others would probably say the same. But still...weren't they going to be surprised when she told them?

Her smile widened as she looked up into the eyes of the man she loved.

"Yes!" Aiden shouted, and punched the air in victory. "She said yes!"